A
MOMENT
OF INSIGHT

SUVRAT J BHARGAVE, M.D.

A Moment of Insight

This book is not intended as a substitute for medical advise. The readers should regularly consult a physician in matters relating to their health. This is particularly important with respect to any symptoms that may require diagnosis or medical attention.

The stories depicted here do not represent any one patient's account but are compilations of hundreds of patients and are created to represent identifiable patient types.

First edition 2018

Published in the USA by Pinnacle Press

eBook ISBN: 978-1-7336005-8-3
Paperback ISBN: 978-1-7336005-3-8
Hardback ISBN: 978-1-7336005-0-7
Audio ISBN: 978-1733-6005-6-9

Library of Congress Control Number: 2019931037

A Moment of Insight

Cover Design

by 100 Covers
www.100covers.com

Interior Design and eBook Formatting

by A.L. Lovell
www.beechhousebooks.com

TABLE OF CONTENTS

NOTE FROM THE AUTHOR

This book is meant to be a conversation. I invite you to continue the dialogue through thoughtful introspection and your notes of reflection.

SB

ACKNOWLEDGEMENTS

To my courageous patients—thank you for exposing your fears, for taking a chance, and for sharing your stories. I honor every tear, cherish every smile, and appreciate every insight.

To Carolyn C, Angie G, Lakshmi J, Janet F, and my dear friends and family near and far—thank you for encouraging a one-of-these-days dream into a chapter-turning reality.

To my dearest parents—you not only loved me completely, but you taught me the many ways for love to be shared. On behalf of every patient that ever felt cared for, I thank you for showing me how.

To my loving children, Avya and Avik—beyond every moment of doubt on this writer's journey was the determination of a father to pass wisdom along. I don't expect you to agree with all that I have written, and I look forward to hearing what you will learn through your own mistakes and successes. But these are the lessons that have proven most valuable to me, and what is most priceless should be shared with the most precious.

To my soulmate and muse, Kali—I entered this marriage feeling indebted. You offered me the space to step forward so that we would instead walk an adventurous and spiritual path together, as equals, and side by side. The secret to a fulfilling union is the mutual willingness to be vulnerable and the guarantee to hold one another's spirits when doing so. You've done that in the most amazing ways. I can walk any journey as long as your hand is in mine.

PREFACE
Detectives and Psychiatrists

What do you want to be when you grow up? Kids want the excitement that comes from being a firefighter, a pilot, a military hero, a doctor, or a forensics investigator. But what if more people understood that psychiatrists and detectives are actually flip sides of the same coin?

Detectives look for clues and then put a story together.

Psychiatrists listen to stories and then pick out the clues.

Detectives rely on tangible evidence.

Psychiatrists deal with intangible wounds.

Detectives train to view their surroundings with suspicion.

Psychiatrists work best when they put all judgment aside.

Despite the dichotomies, the ultimate endeavor of both is the same. Detectives and psychiatrists repeatedly ask tough questions to get to the truth. We are seekers, and that ought to be thrilling.

However, as a psychiatrist practicing for a few decades now, I have never seen a person enter my office charged with enthusiasm. No one sprints into the room with a mission to solve life's greatest mysteries. Of course they don't.

Misery is exhausting. Anxiety is overwhelming. Struggle is disheartening. Trauma is devastating. Compounding the dismal circumstances that accompany most patients is the burden of shame for having to see a psychiatrist at all. There is no thrill in the notion that I am broken and alone.

But . . . what if?

What if this culmination of dilemmas is the opportunity to solve not just the current problem in life but to decipher the most worthwhile questions of life itself? What if the greatest growth can only come when you are most outside your comfort zone? What if the true essence of your journey is beyond any one moment or event that is currently taking place? What if the greatest gains come through the biggest losses? And what if you were never broken and never alone?

Patients usually walked through my door out of curiosity. Each one has questions about what is happening and how to fix it. And despite age, gender, background, or circumstance, they come to see what may be possible. Adversity may have prompted the initial appointment, but the internal drive to search for understanding brings them back. And as long as they come back, we keep digging for answers. We want solutions, so we keep asking questions.

How come? What now? Why me?

As the investigation grows, the questions get deeper.

What's the point? What can I do? When did this start? When will it end? How can I let go? What does this say? Who am I?

Session after session, what I've learned is that solutions don't just appear, but when you ask questions, you inevitably find answers. Through moments of woe come pieces of wisdom. A lot has changed in how we live our lives, but wisdom is as valuable as ever. We have more platforms and forums to speak, learn, and share, yet we are guarded, defensive, and judged. The cost of such self-preservation is a blockade in the flow of wisdom. If we gain worthwhile insight, we ought to distribute it. After all, if the pursuit for answers reveals truths, and if truths by definition are universal, then someone else may benefit from the insight I've gained in my experiences with my patients—and myself. Conversely, it would be in my best interest to hear what you have learned.

Generations' worth of knowledge used to flow across kitchen tables. An engaging conversation resulted in a back-and-forth of ideas, which is harder to manage in the overstimulated and distracted world of today. However, rather than lamenting how things were done in the good old days, we should focus on how best to distribute wisdom now. Whether it was across the kitchen table then or is done across the Internet now, wisdom is best dispensed through stories.

As a psychiatrist, I have heard thousands of stories. These are not the cleaned-up versions that people would have others believe. These are tales of authenticity. It's hard to hide in a psychiatrist's office, but it is possible. Through denial, manipulation, or unwillingness, there are some who avoid the truth, but transformation begins with transparency. You can fool the world, but don't fool yourself.

Patients have detailed some of the worst circumstances, the most challenging stressors, and the deepest emotions. They have shared out of necessity. When you are at your wits' end, you dare to be vulnerable. My patients have had the courage to put their defenses aside and be raw in the telling of their stories. Some were ready to do so during the very first encounter, while others needed a more gradual process to chance being real. While every patient is assured confidentiality, vulnerability requires more than a contract of secrecy. It requires proof that what will be shared will be held in trust, will be received without judgement, and will never come at the cost of one's dignity. That is the promise I make. And with that oath in place, we begin to investigate.

We start with general questions. What brings you in? These are the surface-level accounts, which present the current problem or state the chief complaint. It is the work of a psychiatrist to listen for the opportunity to dig deeper, and then it is up to the patient to delve further from there. The deeper questions, however, inspire the greatest insights. And the fruit of this labored endeavor is insight. The cracked opening in one's way of thinking, feeling, or behaving, which allows a deeper intuitive understanding. Insight is the power to see with renewed clarity. It means shedding light on a piece of evidence that was always there but never acknowledged. Unlike a detective's pursuit, though, insight requires shining a spotlight within.

For as long as I can remember, I have questioned the "within." More accurately stated, I have questioned myself. There's a fine line between curiosity and doubt. My child self was certainly curious. I wanted to learn, and I sought understanding. But in many instances, the knowledge that I gained was meant to reassure doubt. If I worried about something happening to me or my family, then I looked for information that it would all be okay. If I doubted my ability to perform, then I found what I needed to pass and practiced it until I did. Up to a point, my anxiety propelled me to act; a healthy dose of anxiety got me through medical school! But constant doubt takes its toll, too. Also, curiosity inspired by fear isn't very objective. Beyond any temporary moment of reassurance and respite, anxious people tend to filter out information and interpret the data around them to confirm their worst fears. I had definitely done so. My anxiety, combined with a dark secret that I tightly held onto, had formed what I believed to be my truth.

But if anxious questioning had formed my story, curiosity had cracked it open. The willingness to question and figure it out over time revealed some amazing possibilities, and witnessing the journeys of so many patients in my office solidified these truths. Who would have thought that such universal clarity could come through a shrink's couch! The intention of this book is to dispense that wisdom. By shining a spotlight on our collective wounds, we also reap the rewards of shared insights.

I am a storyteller. I tell patient stories. I give you my own. But A Moment of Insight isn't any one person's tale. It's our collective truth, and now it's time to share our story.

CHAPTER 1

We Are Seekers

Where's a good guru when you need one?

As an enthusiastic seeker on a quest to understand life's toughest questions, let's start with that one.

Through the eyes of conventional storytellers, I would imagine my search for a wise teacher taking me on an arduous journey to a faraway land. I picture the Walk of a Million Steps, a back-to-basics trek up a steep mountain, and I see myself endure the hardships of being one with nature, including the personal sacrifice of a no-hair-dryer appearance. I envision that moment along the path where I consider giving up but then get a miraculous universal sign that reassures me: the Wise One resides just around the corner of my desperation. In my mind's eye, I see myself approaching this guru, who is enthralled in a meditative trance, and while I desperately want to throw myself at his feet and cry out for the truth, I recognize this test of patience as another rite of passage before I am enlightened, and therefore, I decide to wait it out.

After days of quietly observing the Meditating Man, my presence is acknowledged through the gentle gaze of my newfound master, who softly inquires, "What is your question, my child?"

"Oh, Great One, I seek the meaning of life."

My guru offers a faint smile and a twinkled expression in his eyes. Then, as if pulled back into the ecstasy of meditation, his eyelids slowly close, and he whispers, "There's no place like home ..."

What?

I wake up from my imagined quest and feel a sense of relief in knowing that, while valuable insights may come, for some, through an actual trek or journey, the potential for life's biggest lessons can be found within the comforts of our homes or within the workings of our day-to-day lives. And I realize that teachers and gurus meet us along the way, even when we aren't actively looking, if we choose to see them. It has also been my experience that some of the most profound understandings come through the most unexpected and unlikely sources.

Psychiatry has been my greatest spiritual teacher.

Now there's a statement that I never could have anticipated making when I first began this career! Still sounds improbable that, after all the ideas and practices I was exposed to in my childhood and across my young adult life, a specialty of medicine that treats mental illness could be the venue for life's greatest lessons to unfold. I was raised in a culture where concepts such as karma, destiny, and purposeful living were round-table discussions over dinner. As a preteen, I was practicing yoga poses (can't imagine doing a headstand now), instructed in the disciplines of meditation (exchanging stolen goofy glances with my brother as my grandfather focused on his mystic third eye), and taught the benefits of Ayurvedic remedies (clearly what's good for you doesn't often taste that way). But even with these enriching discussions surrounding me, I was more interested in learning the lessons that were necessary to pass high school, not the lessons of spirituality.

In college, I took classes in psychology and sociology that explored the theories of child development, personality disorders, and human relationships, which were all fascinating subjects, but they did little to enrich my soul. I went on to psychiatry rotations in medical school, during which I bonded with schizophrenics in locked facilities over games of ping-pong and was intrigued enough about the workings of thoughts and behaviors that I pursued a residency program in the field. During the hands-on but grueling training of my residency years at Duke University, I came to truly appreciate the symbiotic relationship between physical health and emotional well-being but still never factored in spiritual balance. Finally, I entered private practice, ready to take care of others but naive to the spiritual teachings that would soon come my way.

As a rookie, I entered the field with the sincere hope of providing healing, and I specifically expected to do some teaching along the way, but the amount of learning has been a surprising joy and an immense source of gratitude. I assumed that I had gained what I needed to know through the grueling years of medical school and residency, but let's face it: there's learning, and then there's LEARNING. And if psychiatry has been my university, my patients have been some of my best professors. Furthermore, in this "School of Psychiatry," as I like to call it, lessons aren't documented in the pages of a textbook; the most valuable teachings and the most profound spiritual lessons have revealed themselves through discussions. For me, the spoken words have been more powerful than the written ones. Real, open, vulnerable conversations which, much like the fall-to-your-knees prayers of desperation, yield the deepest windows to wisdom. The bond between psychiatrist and patient has become the doorway to a raw place of connection—not just between two people but between two seekers of truth.

I am a psychiatrist. I see people in my office who are feeling discouraged, distraught, and empty. I help children who are experiencing extreme fear, uncontrolled rages, and difficult life circumstances. I meet with couples who feel disconnected, and with individuals who describe a lack of drive or purpose. I treat those who are overcome with anxiety, and I witness the debilitating effects of depression.

Each thinks that they are alone and that no one can understand the irrational feelings and desperate thoughts within their minds. As if no one else could have a case as unusual or severe as what they are experiencing. However, within the four walls of my office, session after session, these people describe the common threads of a shared tapestry. *We truly are more alike than we are different.*

We are all struggling with the same dilemmas and asking the same questions. We've all questioned life's purpose. We've all felt overwhelmed. We've all been weighed down by our secrets. We've all second-guessed our relationships. We've all felt victimized by outside forces that aren't within our control. We've all doubted our worth.

Anxiety is the disease of doubt. It is the disease of second-guessing, but there are lessons to be learned that start with doubt. The greatest spiritual leaders and the most enlightened teachers started their evolved journeys with questions, and anxiety will make a person ask some of the deepest ones. *Why me? What's next? What if?*

Depression is a condition that leads to a person feeling sad, hopeless, discouraged, frustrated, and empty. It can dramatically impact how a person thinks, feels, and acts. In the depths of despair, more questions arise. *What's the point? Why do bad things happen? How will it end?*

People come to me asking so many questions and longingly seeking answers. What starts out as an evaluation for depression or anxiety usually leads my patients and me down a path *away from* surface-level projections that we give our friends, colleagues, and neighbors that "all is well." We delve instead into life's biggest questions—the ones that we've tried our hardest to ignore.

We are seekers.

And the most basic common thread that brings people to my office is the desire for change. Anyone suffering wants the pain to end. I have had patients wonder out loud, "How much worse could it get?" I have surprisingly been asked many times, "Do I have to hit rock bottom before this gets better?" Anyone going through a difficult time wants it to get better and will do anything to have it be so. It is precisely that desperation that has led to the most profound lessons. In the worst of times and during the peak of suffering, there is a defenseless rawness which begs relief and bares open the soul to receive. The good news is, you *don't* have to hit rock bottom, but you *do* have to experience a crucial moment for change to occur. The essential first step toward change is what I call a "Moment of Insight."

CHAPTER 2
What Is a Moment of Insight?

A Moment of Insight is a crack in the window of one's thinking. It's a pause in one's perception. It's a profound second of rational clarity where emotion is set aside. <u>It is a moment of realization in your mind that a certain way of thinking, feeling, or behaving is no longer working for *you*.</u> The fact that it may not be working for someone else in your life is secondary; change can start to manifest itself in a meaningful way only if you see what is not working for *you*.

During the course of my psychiatric practice, I have witnessed countless patients having those moments. Sometimes the moment of clarity is glaringly obvious, where the expression on a person's face abruptly conveys that they "got it." In some instances, the sign is a physical gesture, like a head tilt, a wrinkled forehead, or sitting back in one's chair, which lets me know there has been a shift. I've had people proclaim, "I never thought of it that way … that's true … huh, maybe." And then there are the Moments of Insight that I never saw coming.

The patient who taught me about the importance of this crucial step, and who made me ponder what I would term a Moment of Insight, was a woman being abused by her husband. As is the case with most of my patients, she had initially come to see me when her anxiety became unbearable. She described in detail the physical sensations of her panic attacks. The racing of her heart, the uncontrollable shaking, the rush of thoughts, the wave of dread, and the intense breathing. Some of these episodes came at the most unexpected moments, but she had also come to recognize that she had certain triggers for them as well. Unfortunately, these were triggers that ultimately couldn't be avoided, such as the routine of getting ready for bed or times of transition, like heading home from work.

She hadn't disclosed the domestic violence until many sessions into our work together. On the day that she did, I remember her looking more anxious than I'd ever seen her, almost as if she were going to have one of her most intense panic attacks yet. In hindsight, it hurts even imagining the apprehension she must have felt as she prepared to disclose her secret, and the fear about my possible reaction, the grueling embarrassment of her reality. However, in her desperation to feel better and her hope that I could offer relief if I knew all the facts, she found the courage to take a chance and to let someone into her authentic misery. For all the anxiety she'd felt at the beginning of the session, I could see her relief by the end of the appointment, her face awash with tears.

For the next year, I offered my support, my encouragement, and my resources, but for all her spoken desire to change, her overwhelming fear kept her rooted, and the truth is, I would find myself feeling discouraged and frustrated for and by her.

Then, on one particular session, she was recounting the latest episode of abuse where she was again pushed to the ground, stepped on, and pummeled with potent words of disgrace. Until finally, he spat on her.

He. Spat. On. Her.

She had barely gotten the words out when I instinctively coiled back, much as you may have, and before I could filter myself, I sadly let out a simple comment for this soul that I had come to know and care about: "That is such a violation of basic respect." She stared back bewilderedly at first. Then, with a sense of calm that almost scared me, she answered, "Yeah, it is, isn't it?" She stood up with conviction and declared that she needed to go. She reassured me, thanked me, and said she would see me soon, all in a few short words. And then she left.

I called the next day to check on her and to understand what had happened. She explained that my reaction had been a "jolt" to her. She had been abused by her husband multiple times, and each time, she had accepted it as more punishment for the things that she had done to upset him. Or as an extension of the abuse she'd experienced from her father. Or as further proof from the universe that she was unworthy and unlovable. But, somehow, my statement had given her clarity that this act was a violation of basic respect. It wasn't an extension of HER story. It was an issue of basic respect that all beings deserve. She could now see her situation from the perspective of someone on the outside looking in. She kindly expressed gratitude, and as I hung up the phone, I thought: *really?*

Of all the professional advice that I had dispensed, *that* was the shift?

As grateful as I was, I was baffled. My thoughts began to flow. What had made that instance the pivotal moment? How could I make it happen again? What else have I said that carried more weight than I had realized? Wait a minute ... what has someone else said to *me* that was a turning point in my own life? After all, I have had many patterns in my life that weren't working for me but that I had perpetuated and then felt stupid for doing so. What made me finally change them? What more could I change? What did I need to look at differently—from the outside looking in?

This woman—a "professor" in my School of Psychiatry, if you will—made me appreciate the essential role of a Moment of Insight. The crucial moment when emotion is set aside to allow for a shift in clarity. It is a realization that this way of thinking, feeling, or behaving isn't working. It is an awareness that inspires change.

These moments may happen in a dramatic, lightning-bolt instant——what Oprah would rejoice as an "aha moment"——as was the case for the abused woman I described. Or they may subtly sneak up and nudge us to look at something differently. I believe Moments of Insight can occur all the time, every day, and in all kinds of ways, but we have to be willing and open to see them. They can come through sources of information: a good book, a knowledgeable expert, or a trusted mentor. They can come through light moments, such as the lyrics of a song stuck in your head or a playful exchange among friends. But I believe some of the most powerful Moments of Insight come through thoughtful discussion —through the words that someone says to you, or even through your own words that were said to someone else but meant to be heard by you. Psychiatry has gifted me with opportunities for real, raw, and rich discussions, and as a result, I have witnessed countless moments and benefitted from my own moments as well. What has been another unexpected joy is the realization that most of us need insight for the same patterns of thinking, feeling, or behaving. *We are all more alike than we are different.*

The purpose of this book is to shine a light on our collective wounds. To spotlight the soulful struggles that we all share. As I reassure those patients who come to see me, the reason to authentically examine our hurts rather than continue to cover them up is to *understand, express, and release.* As the School of Psychiatry dictates, the journey requires being vulnerable and aware, but through the promise of hope, we can anticipate valuable insights along the way.

CHAPTER 3
A Bus Ride to Insight

Who am I?

Turning one's life around means balancing discouragement with hope. So before we can embark on a path toward transformation, we have to reflect on what makes us worthy already. After all, we are looking to evolve ourselves, not to discard completely the essence of who we are.

But who are we really? That is the difficult question to explore here first. The task of answering it isn't easy, but the rewards are tremendous. Once you can answer the question "Who am I?" you won't need others to define it for you. You can free yourself from the reliance of what others think of you. You can strip away any false perceptions you've created and more clearly understand what you have to offer. You can identify your unique gifts and commit to using them in order to live more authentically. You can do all that, but *first*, you must ask yourself the question:

If you found your own guru sitting on the mountain top holding the secret answers to life's deepest questions, what would you ask him?

Surely, you wouldn't waste the Wise One's time with the day-to-day questions that clutter your routine thoughts: *What should I have for dinner tonight? How can I get the kids through their homework? What color brings out my eyes?* I imagine that even the most patient of evolved teachers would toss you off the mountainside for bringing such trivial concerns. Yet, the active chatter in our minds would have us believe that these matters are highly important.

Let's put our humanities aside, get into our space of Zen, and try it again.

- Close your eyes.
- Listen to your breath as you inhale and feel it expand your chest.
- Exhale with ease and give your breath the freedom to release at its own slow pace.
- Do it again while imagining inspiration in the form of beautiful energy flowing in and all negativity flowing out.
- Take the time that you need to repeat this cycle until the chatter has a chance to settle.

When we go deep to listen to the questions that matter the most to our souls, the one we often find crying out is "Who am I?"

It would seem that, for most patients I see, who they understand themselves to be depends on what they are doing or what is happening in their lives at any given moment. Their identities are tied to the world around them. Many of my youngest patients believe that who they are depends on what they do. So, they are good if they bring home good grades, but they are bad if they got in trouble with the teacher. Adults in my practice have trained themselves to answer "Who am I?" based on the roles they play. You may be an employee, unless you are fired. You may be a spouse, unless you get a divorce. You may be a busy parent, until your child grows up.

Most patients don't contemplate the question at all until they *have* to. You may be fine, until you are sick. You may be satisfied, until you are desperate. You may be happy, until you are depressed. In each of these cases, it took adversity to make a person reflect inwardly, to realize that they have lost who they truly are. Thankfully, who we are isn't nearly as fluid as all that.

One of my greatest Moments of Insight, a pivotal shift in my awareness that would change my perception and, therefore, my life, occurred when I was in college, and it involved this heavy notion of "Who am I?" And it, too, came through adversity.

I attended the University of Georgia, a big southern university with a proud tradition of football and tailgating, all of which left me feeling out of place most of the time. I wasn't miserable throughout the four years, thanks to some truly fantastic friendships, some successful academic achievements, and the ideal location. It was far enough from home to challenge my dependency but close enough for me to visit my parents whenever I needed, yet I still struggled in my mind to fit in.

One morning, as I was riding the bus to the other side of the campus, my usual monologue of self-criticism blared in my head. I was an expert at noting my faults. I don't know why I considered it a badge of honor to be "my own worst critic." Among the negative statements that bombarded my mind was: *Everyone here thinks you're looking really* _____. I can't remember now what the insult of the day was, but just fill in the blank. I do remember that it had been raining, so knowing me, I was probably preoccupied with having a bad hair day, and the word was likely "ugly."

This type of discussion in my head was certainly not unusual. But for some reason, this time, I responded to it differently.

Three simple words came to mind: *you really think?* Those three words brought the negative thought loop to a sudden stop. Instead, I found myself rationally questioning my doubts. Could it really be that EVERYONE on this bus was looking at me? And could they really all be thinking about what I looked like? Did my frizzy hair *really* hold that kind of power?

I was experiencing a Moment of Insight, and it allowed me to objectively look around the bus and survey the reactions of those around me. I quickly concluded that not only were my peers *not* staring, but truthfully no one had even noticed that I had gotten on the bus! I wanted to laugh out loud. Relief flooded my head, and I rejoiced at my anonymity. I thought happily, *You're really not that important!*

I could feel my clarity building and desperately wanted to confirm my revelation further, so I skipped my next class. I sat on that bus and charged myself with the task of watching others come and go with an objective perspective on their reactions to me. Once again, people got on and off without giving me, or my hair, any consideration.

It was great news. Not only was I completely irrelevant (who would have thought that I would treasure such a notion?) but if I were being completely honest, there may have even been one or two who, through a nod or subtle smile, briefly sent me a positive vibe. In fact, the only person who gave me a critical glance was the bus driver gazing at me through the rearview mirror, which prompted my hour-long experiment to finally end.

I got off the bus and sat on a nearby bench. That day brought immense relief on one hand, and on the other, I had never felt so sad. I was faced with the reality that I had spent so many years defining myself mostly on my perceived reactions and opinions of others. In my desire to please, I would modify who I thought I was based on who was around. In that moment, it hit me: if my perception of what others thought was itself flawed, and I was basing myself on that, then who exactly was I? The freedom that my Moment of Insight had granted me was exhilarating, but the realization that I had lost my authentic self was terrifying and depressing.

Over the years, countless patients have sat in front of me, especially during times of major transitions in their lives, and described feeling "empty." That was exactly how I felt in that moment. It's a powerful word that summarizes an all-encompassing sense of loss and a spiraling vortex of hopelessness. It is a cornerstone symptom of depression, and how could it not be? If a person is questioning the very definition of his being, how could he summon the drive and motivation necessary to engage in life? And if the repeated forgone conclusion to every turn in life is "What's the point?" then how could that empty person not contemplate suicide? Or, at the very least, begin to fear where all of this might be leading?

Emptiness comes from the complete inability to answer "Who am I?" Sure, our day-to-day existence provides enough distractions to endure many moments, but what happens when you are alone with yourself? Most of us don't like an awkward silence in the course of a discussion, and we desperately reach for any topic to keep the flow going. Often, the comments we blurt out make the moment even more awkward! Well, what wouldn't we do when silence is a reminder of our internal emptiness?

As a psychiatrist, I have heard the judgment that we place on the actions of others, but going down the line of thinking that accompanies emptiness, the actions of a depressed person are natural reactions to losing one's sense of self. I have met many people who engage in surprising, risky, and sometimes dangerous behaviors. Without a sense of *Who am I?,* the natural progression is, *Why does it matter?*

Thrill-seeking brings to mind skydiving and bungee jumping, but for many patients that I see, a release or a rush of adrenaline comes through other types of actions that can result in self-harm. There are many who would escape by indulging in mind-altering substances: alcohol to "unwind," marijuana to "chill," or painkillers to "numb." I see patients who resort to sexual promiscuity, where the greater the risk, the greater the excitement, or the "passion" of the moment allows judgment to be put aside. And then there is a growing population of patients who engage in self-injury—those who cut, burn, and mutilate themselves purposefully. Thankfully, these self-injurious behaviors are not meant to be attempts at suicide. If you ask any cutter why he or she does so, there are usually two explanations. Either the goal was to NOT feel something or to FINALLY feel something.

—••—

Emme is a high-school girl who first began seeing me when her parents noticed her becoming more withdrawn and unmotivated. Like many adolescents, Emme had pulled away from spending time with her family and was disinterested in her schoolwork. But she was also disconnected from peers and was not engaging in the activities that interest most other kids her age. The uncertainty of life after high school was looming, and she was tired of the social games that either led to "drama" among her peers or became one more reminder of her failings.

Like all other areas of her life, Emme was indifferent about her sessions with me, not resisting but also not engaging very much in the process. She readily acknowledged her apathy, recognizing that she felt flat and did not have much range of emotion. Eventually, she confided that, at various points in her life, she had cut herself. She knew other girls in her school were doing the same thing, and what had begun as a curiosity became an avenue for experiencing *some* feeling in an existence which otherwise was devoid and numb. Using a pin to make superficial cuts to her upper arm or thigh gave her the ability to finally feel, even if the sensation that she first felt was pain. That was the beginning of our therapeutic journey: we agreed on the shared goal to understand what kept her from *feeling* and how we could help her do so again.

---••---

Emme's story reflects a crossroads where most of us find ourselves at some point. She was seeking an existence among others but wanting a stable sense of herself that had little to do with others. Much like my younger self on that bench on my college campus, she knew, as I had known, that there was no distracting from the uncertainty anymore. It was time for her to answer "Who am I?" in order to get her back to her true self, just as my younger self had to do many years before.

I am generally a positive person; I can now embrace being in the "half-full" camp, although I'm still not a big fan of the term "rose-colored glasses," and so even my discouraged and empty younger self could start feeling reassured with the possibilities of what could come next. My Moment of Insight could finally allow ME to know ME without the burden of perceived opinions of others.

For all the effort that I had put into understanding other people, I deserved to understand myself more fully.

This process is harder for some people than others. The good news this:

Who you are is who your soul already knows you to be.

CHAPTER 4

Socrates Is in the House

On the day of my Moment of Insight, I was reminded of my grandfather and how, even at a young age, he would push me to consider my core self.

I was blessed to have my grandparents living with us from a very young age. A household of several generations living under the same roof was not unusual for families in India, but as a child born and raised in Georgia, I knew it was not the norm in America. My home was special and unlike what even most of my Indian-American friends had known.

My grandfather was a deeply religious man, someone who taught us rituals. Moreover, he was a highly disciplined person, who had incorporated religious teachings into the fabric of his daily life. Mornings were spent doing yoga, sitting in meditation, and chanting prayers. This routine took several hours, starting before sunrise, and then was repeated in the evenings. I would see him begin each meal with prayer, and then he would set a bite of his meal aside as an offering before he ever took the first bite. While my grandmother relished the social aspects and the bonding of holidays, he emphasized the "Reason for the Season" before I had ever heard that phrase. He wanted us to understand the meaning behind the rituals and our actions.

What I realized, though, as I got older was that my grandfather was devoutly religious but also deeply spiritual. I see religion as a practice of trying to understand God, and spirituality as a practice of wanting to experience God. This became apparent to me as he challenged me with endless, deep questions. I was convinced my grandfather was the reincarnated spirit of Socrates! I don't want to characterize him as a saint, though; my inability or reluctance to dig deep would elicit exasperation routinely. Many of these trying times originated from one of the simplest yet powerful questions he would ask me repeatedly: "Who are you?" As a kid who wanted to just go back to reading comic books. I made several attempts over many years to give him the truest, and fastest, answer. "I am your grandson" was offered as an appeal to his ego.

But, to my dismay, the reply would be, "So, if I were to die today, would you cease to be?"

"Fine. I am Suvrat."

Without pause, "So, if you changed your name, would you become someone else?"

Before I even got the next attempt at a response out of my mouth, I recognized that "I am a student" didn't stand a chance … because, obviously, who would I then be when I graduated? Ugh!

My grandfather would eventually offer an answer.

He would take my hand in his, hold it up to my chest, and very matter-of-factly say, "You are God. God sits within you right here. Just as He sits within me, within everyone. Not just within everyone but within everything. You are God."

Long pause. Hmmm ...

"Okay, may I go now?" I said this on the *inside*, of course.

I can't imagine, if I'd voiced such a thought, where it might have left him in his desire to bring me enlightenment, but that seed, which was planted all those years ago, would begin to sprout on that day at college many years later.

Even in that darkest moment as a student who recognized that, in two decades of living, I knew little to nothing about who I was, I could start with the notion that I had been created as something Divine. I wasn't quite ready for "I am God." Boy, were we in trouble if that were the case! But I had heard it enough, and I couldn't deny that there was a miracle or a supreme force that had created me. Surely, I couldn't be a fluke or a coincidence. I mean, just look around—there is incredible intricacy everywhere!

As an optimist and empathetic person, I could also acknowledge that there must be some good in everyone. So, if God had taken the time to specifically create me and if He is an all-loving, benevolent being, He must have bestowed me with some traits that were good. At that point in my life, I wasn't ready to call them "strengths" (I thought it was egotistical to focus on my strengths, even though I now realize that it completely isn't) but I could call them "gifts." I understood that God had brought me onto this earth and given me certain gifts; that is, He had equipped me with certain innate traits and qualities, just as He had done for each of His creations.

And it isn't that my gifts are better or worse than anyone else's. I have my gifts, and you have yours. From the moment I took my first breath in this world until I take the last one, I am gifted, and so are you.

CHAPTER 5
The Five Gifts
∞

So, what did I figure my gifts to be?

In a gesture that I can only call divine, I charged my twenty-year-old self with a task. I needed to come up with a list of my five gifts. Why five? Well, anything less sounded like I was taking the easy way out (there was "my own worst critic" again), and anything more sounded like a real stretch for me and my empty self. So, I would do five, and I even gave myself a deadline—ten days from my Moment of Insight. These would be traits and qualities that were innate to me, regardless of who was around, how old I was, or what was happening in my life.

The process wasn't easy, but I did it. I had written my five gifts on a piece of paper, and the list stared back at me. The exhausting act of determining this list had been valuable if for no other reason than to highlight just how skewed my perspective had become—it should never take anyone that long to recognize his positive traits! As worthwhile as that lesson was, I realized it wasn't enough to identify my gifts, but if those five characteristics were God-given, I certainly should not waste them. I needed to use them.

Once my catalog of five gifts was compiled, I knew

that I needed to commit myself to them. I never wanted to feel so off balance again. After decades of being my own worst critic, it was high time to become my own best friend.

I literally carried the list of five gifts around with me at all times until I no longer needed to refer to it in any instant. Once I had committed my gifts to memory, I decided that in order to fully cultivate my authentic identity, I needed to surround myself with activities, interactions, opportunities, and goals that made the most of these five gifts. I recall feeling excited by the task, almost as if I couldn't wait to see if I really had these traits and curious to discover their potential and the "new me," whom I had actually been all along.

What I realize now, in hindsight, is that this challenge had caused me to switch perspectives from what I didn't do well to a demonstration of what I did have to offer. I also found that the exercise gave me a strategy to get through moments of discouragement and negativity. For example, on a day where I was coming down hard on myself, I would charge myself with the task of picking any one of the five gifts and then going out into the day with a resolve to use it. In doing so, I would reaffirm that it really *was* one of my innate characteristics.

If *empathy*, the first gift that I had written down on that piece of paper, was the gift of the day, I would purposefully seek opportunities to use it. While at the grocery store, when the cashier would ask the seemingly obligatory questions, "How are you? Did you find everything okay?" my intention was to not just give an obligatory answer back. Instead, I would use my gift of empathy and offer, "Yes, my day has been pretty good. What about yours? You look quite busy." In the few minutes that followed, I noticed that what could have been another mundane back-and-forth became a pleasant moment of connection between two strangers, initiated through the use of empathy, one of my cherished five gifts. I discovered that the opportunities to use my gifts were plentiful, but I had filtered them out through my negative lens.

———••———

When I talk to patients now in my practice about the importance of a balanced sense of self and the exercise of listing one's five gifts, I give them the same parameters that I had given myself many years ago … and that I had given to Emme as well.

Emme engaged in treatment more genuinely after that pact to help her feel again. She recognized that, as a younger child, she had always been a pleaser. The only child of a couple who argued often and seemed disconnected, Emme had seen that her good behavior not only kept the peace in the household but even facilitated a momentary bond between her parents. Her opportunities to please expanded as she performed well in elementary school. She had come to answer "Who am I?" with "I am a good girl and good student." That is, until she was neither.

Middle school brought a new set of challenges, both

academically and socially. And the growing independence of adolescence resulted in more conflicts with Emme's parents. She had failed her definition of herself, and the emptiness began to grow within her. At the time of our initial appointment, high school was nearing an end, and the future and her role in it were uncertain and discouraging. She agreed that defining herself for others had been too painful, and she reluctantly accepted the task of identifying her five gifts.

The process was difficult for Emme, and she felt frustrated in not being able to list even one trait that was completely and innately hers. I suggested that she think back to her childhood and the times when she felt most *in the zone*. What were the activities and interactions that brought her the most joy and lifted her spirit? She could identify two: reading alone and spending time with her dog. I then asked her what traits of hers contributed to her satisfaction during these examples.

Emme struggled for a while, but eventually she recognized that her *creativity* came through in the form of her imagination as she read, and her *compassion* manifested itself in the caring for and bonding with her pet. This was the beginning of her self-discovery that has Emme now pursuing a career in teaching, which utilizes both these gifts, and other ones she eventually came up with, and a social circle of a few close friends who appreciate who she is authentically.

Your Insights

_____

_____

_____

_____

_____

_____

_____

_____

_____

_____

_____

_____

_____

_____

_____

_____

_____

_____

CHAPTER 6

A Spark of the Divine

The parameters for the Five Gifts exercise are specific. Most importantly, the list should be devised without any input from others. The whole point of the endeavor is to find out about yourself, not to find out what others think of you. Remember, you want to answer "Who am I?" … not "Who do they need me to be?"

If five seems like too many to begin with, give yourself the flexibility to make an inventory of two or three gifts to start with, as Emme had done. If you need more time, allow an extension of a few days. I do recommend a timeframe, though; otherwise, people mean well but don't prioritize themselves to follow through. It is crucial to set yourself up to succeed at this. The last thing you need is further proof of your failings when overcoming the burden of your negative self-image. Success builds on success, and you want to feel the momentum building. The possibility of "getting to know you" should entice you.

Can you add to the five? Absolutely! In fact, my hope for you is that your journey of self-discovery will lead to the realization that because we are each a beautiful reflection of a force so divine, we all carry an abundance of gifts. Don't let yourself develop your list as a comparison to other people's lists. My gifts are not better or worse than yours, but I overflow with my set, and you with yours.

Can you erase a gift from your original list? In the interest of avoiding the pressure of commitment that may keep you from getting started, let's allow for the possibility, but if your instinct directed you to add it in the first place, it's probably your own fear or doubt that makes you second-guess the trait. Remember, these gifts are the core of who you are, and who you are is constant. As you come to know yourself better, you will add more, but gifts, by definition, don't go away.

Once your list is compiled, commit yourself to act on your gifts as much as possible. When Emme had an urge to cut herself, she would instead pick a gift and use it. When she needed a reminder of her true self, she did the same. The more she practiced, the better she became. At first, her gift of creativity was best expressed through the arts, such as drawing, but over time, Emme celebrated her skills in organization as another creative process. By expanding her focus, opportunities were readily available.

I hope this process will be as intoxicating for you as it was for me! I hope you will get to the point where you no longer doubt your innate worth and where you rely on that stability to deal with life's everyday turbulence. I hope you will be able to condition your mind to recognize undeniable gifts when you see them and to mentally pat yourself on the back each time you use one. Not only that, but I hope you will see gifts in others and to pat them on their backs with the sincere gesture of a compliment.

Imagine what a treasure it would be to raise children to recognize their own innate worth and value simply by pointing out their gifts as you see them manifest. Instead of saying, "I am so proud of this report card," you would comment, "Wow! There you go, showing your willingness to work hard again!" Or "See? Your curiosity always pays off!"

It is just like every enlightened scholar has ever said: *loving others starts with loving yourself.*

If I could sit with my grandfather now and he were to patiently ask me once again, "Who are you?" this is what I would answer:

What I know for sure now is that I am a Spark of the Divine. Just as you are a Spark of the Divine, just as that person is, and that one, too.

If the Spirit that sustains all is Divine Consciousness, then I am a Drop of Consciousness. If the higher power is a blinding Light, then I am a Reflection.

And for any who might find all that to be too heavy, I would simply say:

I am a Soul who feels, reacts, and learns just like you, but who sustains itself beyond what is felt, experienced, or acted upon. A constant self.

Who I am is constantly, Divinely, and lovingly good.

CHAPTER 7

The Opposing Force of Fear

What if?

The path of self-discovery and transformation rests on the premise of hope. It's what brings patients to my office —the hope that someone can help. It's what allows them to consider treatment—the hope that something will give relief. It's what facilitates their willingness to be vulnerable—the hope that on the other side of suffering lies purpose.

For many patients, the thread of hope is tied to their faith. Even the word "faith" itself implies an inherent belief and trust in a relationship that is Divine. But for many who are struggling, there is a crisis of faith which fills them with doubt and leaves them wondering "What if?"

I am a Spark of the Divine.

I Am.

I do believe that. In fact, I know that. Without a shadow of a doubt.

But if I know that I have that kind of force within me, why am I not fulfilling my Divine destiny? If I know that I have the limitless potential of a never-ending source, why do I hold myself back? If I am a reflection of the Creator, how could I ever deny my worth? And yet, throughout my life, I have. Even when everything around me told me otherwise, I have never given myself that kind of credit.

Even when my parents said so. I am blessed to have grown up in a household where my parents expressed love freely to one another and toward my brother and me. I was convinced that they just loved love! And still...

Even when my teachers said so. I was never the cute kid. I don't mean that to be self- deprecating; I mean, I was fine, but my brother was so cute! I was never the athletic one. It was so much fun hanging around with my circle of friends, until they went outside to play football. I was the smart one. And I had the certificates, the plaques, and the awards to prove it. And yet...

Even when my patients said so. There is nothing as satisfying as seeing a patient who has struggled his entire life evolve, endure, and then thrive. Ironically, people may enter my office on those initial appointments feeling ashamed and embarrassed and expecting to be judged, when the reality is that their courage to be vulnerable and to learn is inspiring. And in the course of those individual journeys, to have played a role in the evolution of a soul's experience is humbling. I have not only felt the satisfaction, but I have been on the receiving end of relieved gratitude and the most heartfelt hugs. But...

To know that I am a Spark and to still doubt myself makes no sense. If God is omnipotent, pure benevolence, then there must be a powerful force opposing it within me as well. Newton's Third Law of Physics dictates that for every action there is an equal and opposite reaction—science is so Divinely ordered! If God is love, then the opposite is fear. That is the only answer I could come up with, and the School of Psychiatry led me there. In the clinical world, the term for fear is "anxiety."

Anxiety. We've all felt it. I know I have.

Some people feel it here and there, while others are gripped by it way too often. Some harness it and see it as a driving force. Others are paralyzed by it and become overwhelmed by its presence. Some give it little thought while many obsess over "What if?"

As a psychiatrist, I see people who are feeling discouraged and distracted, overwhelmed and confused, uneasy and empty. *The Diagnostic and Statistical Manual of Mental Disorders (DSM-5)* is the standard classification of mental disorders used by mental-health professionals in the United States. In other words, the DSM-5 is the bible of psychiatry, which catalogues the multiple conditions that fall under the realm of my corner of medicine. It has quite literally evolved from a pamphlet into a tome of information for psychiatrists, outlining the many disorders that we might treat, but the condition I treat more than any other is anxiety. Whatever patients choose to call it, the devastating and confusing effects of this force bring many exhausted patients to my office every day.

Anxiety doesn't discriminate; it afflicts people of all ages, and it travels across all borders. It does not consider your resources or your circumstances. There is no vaccine.

Anxiety is a hard word to define because it can present differently for different people. For some, it means a feeling of being tense or on edge. For others, it can manifest as excessive worry. Anxious people often describe being overly fearful. Sometimes it means feeling pressured or panicked, or in some cases, it shows up as someone who is obsessive, where a disturbing thought spins and spins as the anxiety builds and builds. For most, anxiety is all of these things: feeling tense, worried, fearful, pressured, panicked, inadequate, and obsessive.

Desperate individuals do their research to figure it out; in today's world, that usually involves an Internet search. They show up in my office convinced they have multiple disorders, when, in fact, they are experiencing multiple manifestations of the same condition. After all, our brains and our souls don't care what we call things; we came up with the words, but the basic experiences of anxiety are the same each time.

At the core of anxiety is doubt. It is a constant second-guessing and an unrelenting series of what-ifs. There is doubt in the mind of the anxious patient about the people and the environment around him, but the force works its way from within. The restless spirits of those with an anxious temperament never feel good enough, and as a result, those who are anxious are always trying to please. They are perfectionistic yet never able to achieve satisfaction. They have set a bar that is so high it can never be achieved. They have held themselves to the ridiculous standard of "give it 110 percent" and then feel exhausted and discouraged when they can't give it. Been there, done that!

An anxious person never feels on solid ground, as if always waiting for the other shoe to drop. So much so that children who first feel its presence are constantly doubting their own safety or that of their loved ones. Obviously, we as parents and adults have to warn our children about potential dangers, but anxious children will take a relatively small possibility and turn it into probability. So, a bad storm means there will be a tornado. Or an upset stomach could lead to vomiting, which could then lead to something much worse. Or the darkness that accompanies falling asleep signals the time when someone *will* (not *could*) break in, or when the monster under the bed will then abduct him.

Anxiety doesn't have to make sense; by definition it is an irrational fear, but it presents in such a full-force way that a person will still respond. Usually that response is to flee, avoid, or seek some type of external reassurance, which for a child might be to cling to a parent, or for an adult, it may be to reach for a drink or seek the protection of a relationship, even an unhealthy one. Anxious people are desperate. That doesn't mean everyone who experiences it will inherently come across as shy, although very many do. In an effort to not be judged and to get a negative spotlight off of them, a doubtful person may put up a facade of assurance and bravado, all the while struggling to "fake it until he makes it." And while most anxious people pull themselves inward, some act out, reflecting the horrible chaos they are experiencing on the inside.

CHAPTER 8

The Fear in His Eyes

This is a story about another patient, whom we shall refer to as Jay.

Jay's story demonstrates the inward push and the outward pull that comes from experiencing anxiety. Jay is an eleven-year-old who was brought by his mother to my office in a moment of crisis. Like most of the young ones that I meet, it surely wasn't Jay's decision to see a psychiatrist; on the contrary, this appointment was the latest spotlight that he dreaded. I must admit I have often wondered what goes through the minds of my patients on that first appointment within the four walls of my office. I can see the apprehension in most of their faces. The confusion in the expressions of some of the kids; the resistance in the body language of others. I can only imagine that many don't know what to expect. I imagine a big percentage of them bombard their parents with questions on the car ride to the office, with one of the most common being: "Am I getting a shot?"

Jay had asked endless questions and had desperately fought his mom from the time he was told of the upcoming office visit, until finally he recognized that further resistance was futile; there was no avoiding this. She was wise not to give too much notice too many days beforehand but also she knew from experience that last-minute plans and changes in routine triggered his anxiety tremendously.

He came into my office withholding eye contact and clinging to his mother. Like most of the kids who enter my room, he was fascinated by the wall of comic-book art and figures that decorate one of the walls, and I was grateful to sense some relief. *"How intimidating could this guy be if he's into superheroes?"* The ambiance of the physical space is meant to convey a place of comfort and reassurance as opposed to the clinical and foreboding expectations that people have brought with them on that initial meeting. And the intention seemed to be paying off, if only for the moment.

His mother explained that Jay had always been a "sensitive" child, both in terms of physical sensations and his emotional responses to the world around him. He wore noise-cancelling headphones around his neck. She went on to describe how, over the years, he had been extremely cautious, wanting to be on the same level of the house as his parents, refusing offers of sleepovers, and struggling to sleep by himself in his own room.

Attempts to attend preschools were met with "too much drama" to be worth it, but then came kindergarten. Once again, mornings were filled with tears and complaints about stomach pain. Sundays were the worst, and Fridays were a relief. The nights before each school day were restless, making the next morning an exhausting endeavor. The patterns continued in this way until finally the sheer desperation of the situation led to a decision to homeschool. While this provided relief, Jay's mom explained they could not maintain the complexities that this created for their family.

Jay's father was serving in the armed forces and away on his third deployment. The family's finances required her to keep a full-time job, and while her employers had been as accommodating as they could to her family's needs during this difficult time, she knew they could not be as understanding for much longer. And then there was Jay's younger brother, who was in a traditional school setting and attended an after-school program until his mom could pick him up.

So, at the beginning of this school year, Jay would have to go back to school. The reactions of times past recurred, but this time, the situation escalated dramatically. Even if his mother could manage to get him into the car in the mornings, Jay would refuse to get out at the school. She detailed a physical struggle, with the principal trying to coerce him on one side and the parent pushing from the other. The scenes were loud and inevitably drew the attention of others in the carpool line and of the kids entering the school. All eyes were on Jay, screaming, crying, and becoming aggressive. For a child who dreaded the spotlight, this was a nightmare!

Indeed, even as his mother described the situation to me during that initial appointment, I could see his anxiety building. He didn't want to wait in the other room while his mother and I spoke. I would suggest breaks and pauses along the way, and I reassured him repeatedly that he would never be judged within those four walls (at the very least), that he was never alone, and that hundreds of other children had described this exact story to me over the years. However, the moments of relief and surprise in hearing these things became weaker and less comforting the longer we all sat together. Finally, Jay began pulling at his mother's arm, grabbing at her clothing, and tugging on her long hair in an intense gesture of needing to leave, ultimately wanting to flee.

I had barely made my suggestion that we take a walk outside, when Jay quickly got up and headed to the door with the two of us following behind. Jay's mom began to apologize but understood my gesturing to her that doing so was not necessary and was actually perpetuating the moment. It has always astounded me how even parents that I have just met fall into the therapeutic dance that I am leading within my office, so that we become a collaborating presence for a struggling child.

I could plainly see the anticipation of freedom that Jay felt as we walked out the front door and into the sunlight, where I could then see the beads of sweat on his forehead and notice his posture change to take in the freshness of the air. I could see this young boy literally trying to catch his breath as his hand went up to his mouth. What I knew for sure in that moment was that this eleven-year-old was having a panic attack.

We agreed to sit on the grass. In a steady tone of voice,

I advised that the three of us take some deep breaths, the kind where we could visualize the breaths starting from the pits of our stomachs, rising gradually through our chests, and then escaping slowly through our pursed lips. After a series of these quiet breaths, we continued the steady process, but this time, I said a word on our inhalation and another one on each exhale. "Let ... Go ... Let ... Go ..."

Several minutes passed by, and I could see the ease of Jay's breathing, bringing him back to his calmer baseline, just as I could see a couple of relieved tears signaling that the chaotic moment had passed.

Whether he would ever come back to see me or not, I told Jay that I wanted him to know what had just happened. I promised him that, while I wasn't smarter than he was, I did have information he didn't have, and once I had passed it on to him, he would have a place to begin to regain some control. I needed him to understand the force that had flooded him was called "anxiety." He could rename it whatever he would like; he could call it "dread" or "fear" or "doubt," or any other word that made sense to him, but he had to call it out. He had to be able to identify it, so that when it entered the room, he would have the chance to see it as anxiety. Otherwise, he would misinterpret it as a signal to react and feed it in the ways that his body and mind had become trained to do.

My suggestion was to think of it as a false alarm. We all have an alarm system within each of us. If I am about to cross a street, my alarm goes off, prompting me to look both ways. I do so, and after seeing that the coast is clear, I turn my alarm off and cross the street. Thank goodness for the alarm; otherwise, I may have wandered into danger carelessly. Anxiety is a false alarm. In this example, it would be as if I were walking in a wide-open, clear pasture when suddenly my alarm goes off. In that second, I have a choice to make. I could start looking around and anticipating, "Maybe there is a car coming; I mean, there are cars that can move on this terrain. Maybe it even passed by and I just missed it, or maybe it's still on its way." Or I could make the choice to recognize this as a false alarm. In THIS moment, at THIS time, there is nothing happening; therefore, despite the overwhelming sensations of the loud bells and whistles, I recognize the false alarm and choose to keep walking.

Don't underestimate how hard this is for someone with anxiety. Every instinct and trained response is to act on it, but the most important first step is to call it out: *this is anxiety.*

To be clear, this is *not* instinct. This is *not* about needing to prepare for impending doom. This is *not* about being ill-equipped to survive. This is *not* about being too weak. This is *not* about others laughing at your distress. This is *not* about being punished. This is *not* about my being alone. This *not* about your greatest fear coming to pass. This is *not* about the beginning of the end.

This. Is. Anxiety.

It's only after you turn an alarm off that you can start to direct yourself back to a state of calmness. Two things happen when we get anxious: our bodies speed up, and our thoughts speed up; therefore, the next plan of action is to calm both down. The most effective, tried-and-true method of calming the body is to take deep breaths. Meditation, yoga, hypnosis, and any other path toward inward tranquility begins with focusing on the breath— that is, purposeful, slow, and deep breathing.

The beauty of this strategy is that it can be implemented anywhere. You have to breathe anyway, so why not breathe purposefully? A child can do this before going to school. An adult can do so before going into a presentation at work.

There are many ways to calm your thoughts down, including prayer, guided imagery, counting, and self-coaching techniques, but in a moment of panic, I find it best to keep things simple. To calm thoughts down at the same time as calming the body down, try linking the inhalations and exhalations with a pair of words. "Let go ... love you ... got this ... I am ..." The words should be particular to you and offer you solace or strength. Clearly, "Oh, no!" wouldn't be a pairing I would recommend!

Too much discussion within an anxious mind lends itself to emotional interpretation or desperation, but simple words maintain focus amidst chaos, and by using the same two words each time, you are conditioning your body and mind to anticipate relaxation mode rather than the trained responses that have fed your anxiety thus far. In other words, "Let go" becomes the counterpoint to "What if?"

Jay didn't know it when we first met, but on that day, Jay had taken a big step in his battle with doubt; he began to recognize it. Over time, he became better at seeing anxiety enter the room, and with practice, he got better at not feeding it. He could also reflect on times when his being "sensitive" was triggered by very real circumstances. He recalled the first time he felt extreme dread. He was three years old, and his family was being split apart. His father was being deployed. A toddler couldn't have any point of reference for this, but every child, especially a sensitive one, looks at the world around him to gauge what is going on and how he should react. Jay knew nothing about war, but he knew that his mother was sobbing, he felt his father's sadness, and he could sense from the hugs that this goodbye was somehow different from the ones that he was used to on most mornings.

What was remarkable to hear from Jay's perspective were all the details. He remembered the tile on the floor. He could describe the color of the walls. He could picture the time of day. And most of all, he could recall the gnawing in the pit of his stomach. The same gnawing that he felt eight years later when going to school.

CHAPTER 9

I Am Not My Fear

For those of us, like Jay, who have experienced anxiety, doubt has plagued our minds from a very early age or, at least, for a very long time. The world has always posed threats, and our ability to survive in it or to be good enough to handle it has always been questionable. I believe we are all born with our individual temperaments, and among those is the tendency to feel anxious. Coming from that perspective, life then introduces very real reasons to be concerned. From the hurt that accompanies a careless fall to a parent's lesson of "stranger danger" to the judgment of a teacher that comes in the form of a failed test grade, we as anxious children have a filter through which we interpret the world around us. And we arrive at the conclusion early on that the world is a dangerous place and that the people in it are able to see through us and notice our inadequacies. Perhaps even before we became aware of the concept of God, much less the complexity of being a Spark of the Divine, we knew fear. In the battle of opposing forces, fear made the first move and then grew from there.

That's the thing about fear; it's a slow-growing, insidious force that speaks to you in your own voice and lingers in your presence. It not only makes you think that it is a part of you, but it convinces you that you ARE your fear. However, once you recognize it and call it out as its own force, you can begin to separate yourself from doubt. Once you start to realize that you are not your fear, you can entertain the question, "Then, who am I?"

There's the Moment of Insight!

In the tipping scale of life, anxious people are top-heavy and loaded down with negativity in the form of doubt, despair, and unease. No wonder it is so exhausting! From that moment when you recognize that you are not your fear and that you have a choice over your thoughts, you can begin to balance out the scale and find thoughts that counter doubt. But you need to start somewhere. Even a pebble adds some weight to the other side.

For some, the first layer of the foundation they will build upon comes through faith or religion——for example, my grandfather's reassurance that God rests within me—but in the course of doubt, many are left uncertain about the nature of a relationship with a higher source, which is fine, too. Instead, perhaps the place to start balancing your doubt is the agreement that you make with yourself to not negate a compliment. Even if you do not see what the other person is praising, commit to yourself that you will not undo it with a dismissive *"He's just being nice."* Instead, I would suggest saying to yourself, *"Borrow on faith."* If you have any faith at all in the kindness of the person giving you positive feedback, then borrow on your faith in them—that they had a reason to say it —and accept it, even if you don't see it. My hope is that you are not only *borrowing* on faith at the time, but also that one day you will actually *see* the compliment and *return* it with a genuine "Thank you."

Another strategy to balance doubt is the Golden Rule in Reverse: *Do unto yourself as you would do unto others*. As experts on fear, anxious people know exactly what to say to others who are having a doubtful moment. After all, being "sensitive" leads to empathy and being a "pleaser" means honing the skill to provide others with what they need. For these reasons, those with an anxious temperament are nurturing toward others, but the default mode for treating oneself falls back to being one's own worst critic. Therefore, in an attempt to balance the presence of fearful thoughts, make the deal with yourself that if you wouldn't say something out loud to someone else, you won't permit it in your inner space, either. Not only should the content of the dialogue in your head match your spoken word, but the tone should be the same as well. Nurturing a person during an anxious crisis elicits a certain tone of voice, whether it is reassuring, loving, or lighthearted. We know that, and we do it in a comforting way for the struggling friend in front of us, but in our own inner episode of anxiety, the tone is often frantic, tense, and condescending.

Support yourself as you would a friend. You are not allowed to be your own worst critic unless you also learn to become your own best supporter. I found out early on in my roles of psychiatrist and parent that *how* I said something was at least as important as *what* I was saying. In both roles, I would have to give difficult feedback at times, but my tone conveyed my good and loving intention. It was so reassuringly effective in my interactions that I adopted and fine-tuned the tone of my own inner voice as well. Any difficult circumstance is better addressed with a level mind and a steadfast tone, and whenever possible, maybe even a lighthearted one. (I may or may not be a funny person in the opinion of others, but in my own thoughts, I am hilarious!)

If you cannot do that, perhaps the place for you to begin balancing doubt starts with the acknowledgment that somewhere in your life, at least at one point in your life, you did something right or experienced a positive moment—so, what brought that on? Was it the utilization of one of your five gifts? Was it the act of doing something for someone else? Or was it the realization, even briefly, that as bad as you have felt or as bad as your circumstances have been, someone else has had it worse? Whatever the case may be, start from that place of gratitude. Even a seemingly small pebble of gratitude can start to counter doubt, and each one of us has ten things we could be grateful for right now: the light coming through the window, the color red, the technology that allows me to turn on a fan when I'm hot, and the breath that I just took. And so on.

For many people, *What if?* is the question that has disproportionately consumed their energies. Once you begin to separate and balance, you know you are not your fear or any one emotion that you experience. You know you are not any one mistake or action that you took. You know you are not the victim of what was done to you or another's judgment of you.

You are so much more, and you always have been.

CHAPTER 10
Proving False Truths

Why Me?

The School of Psychiatry has taught me that true emotional, psychological, and spiritual well-being comes through balance from within. When the balance in understanding oneself is off ——when we are skewed toward only noticing our faults and flaws——there is unease (disease), and when we are focused on the external factors in our lives rather than the internal ones, we set ourselves up to be victims. There is nothing as depressing and anxiety-provoking as the notion that "I am bad" and that "Bad things happen to me."

We've all been victims in some way in our lives; that is, we have all felt that something outside of us has affected our emotional state, our worth, or our destinies. In doing so, we have handed the keys to our own happiness over to something or someone else and resigned to become observers to the unfolding of our own identities. These influences and incidents accumulate over the course of our lifetimes, until they have formed our individual stories. We carry our stories around like a mandatory form of identification or a reflection of our genetic makeup. We often fuse ourselves to them until we *become our stories*, and at the end of every telling of it, we ask, "Why me?"

Let's face it: life happens. We all participate in life, but if your understanding of yourself is based on what happens in your life, then the odds are you will feel uneasy and confused. Furthermore, though we all react to things that happen to us in some way, if your state of contentment is at the mercy of those ever-changing encounters, you are bound to feel unstable. Unless you were surrounded by constant love and sheltered from any struggle, chances are that you have felt unsettled. Even if your circumstances and interactions are currently happy ones, we all know situations change. Life happens.

Most of the kids I have seen in my practice feel victimized by what has happened in their lives. It's not their faults, really; we've taught them to feel so. We have conditioned them to gauge themselves based on action and consequence and to understand themselves based on the evaluation of others. Babies come into this world as internally-aware beings, and then we as adults train them to shift their focus outward. Obviously, there is much to be gained from the social interactions and connections which surround them, especially healthy ones, but how tremendous would it be if their notions of identity and self-worth were well-balanced and internally constant?

Kids are constantly intertwining two very different trains of thought; they mix the idea of "Who I am" with "What I do." These concepts are actually independent of one another. In the young mind, if I fail a test, I am a failure. If I do something wrong, I am bad. When feedback about behaviors or performance is being given during an appointment in my office, I have witnessed kids turning to their parents and clearly asking, "Do you still love me? Are you mad at me?" In response, the mother or father makes it very clear by responding, "I love you, but I don't like your choice." Makes perfect sense, yet I guarantee that while many of those children were relieved to get the reassurance, they didn't truly accept the dividing line between action and identity. The parent meant well, but in the end, the intention of the grown-up is not as important as the interpretation of the child.

These moments are the opportunities for a valuable clarification to be made. *What I do* is constantly changing. In the course of my day, I will make multiple decisions, some of which will work out, while others perhaps not so much. Indeed, I am positive I will make at least two or three mistakes today. For the mistakes I make, I can hope for guilt, remorse, or insight to teach for future reference. In this way, I learn from *what I do*. As fluid as my choices and actions are, *who I am* is Divinely constant. When I tell my child how much I love him, I mean that I recognize all that makes him who he is, and in acknowledgment of those innate qualities, I offer love. Love that does not depend on action but is unchanging. *Who I am* is worthy. Period.

When a person has defined his sense of self based on his actions, it is no wonder that his initial response to making a mistake is to deflect blame. After all, in his line of thinking, when he messed something up, it means that he is a mess-up. And this wouldn't be the first time!

Instead, his self-preserving instinct is to externalize the blame so it becomes someone else's burden. For some who equate action and identity, failing at something can elicit a dramatic response.

As an example, a young boy who perceives letting his team down by striking out during a little-league game may have a full-blown tantrum at home plate. A young girl who couldn't do her homework correctly may start pulling her own hair or hitting herself while calling herself stupid. Or a child who disappointed his parents in some way may desperately shout out that he wishes he were dead or that he wants to kill himself. In each of these cases, validation of self-worth (who I am) was jeopardized by performances not going as planned (what I do.)

What I do is further complicated by the fact that I not only react to what I have done, but I am responding to *what is done* to me. In this way, circumstances that I may have little control over may rock the very foundation of who I understand myself to be. So, a teenager who tried out for the school basketball team but didn't get chosen may respond by feeling that he had failed yet again. On top of that, his inadequacies were noticed by the coach, who "apparently" thought he was not good enough to be on the team. On the other hand, the teenager may have gone into the tryouts convincing himself that he *was* good enough, only to find his whole sense of value challenged by the coach's rejection. Now his disappointment and unease are converted into anger towards the coach who denied him his measure of worth. In either scenario, his pattern of thinking persists. Either he perceives himself as the sum of his mistakes, which are constantly noticed by others. Or, across his lifetime, he is the victim of what others have done to him and, therefore, never became good enough. He forms his story.

I have often counseled patients on the falsehoods from our childhoods that become our truths. In other words, we introduce a hypothesis to our young selves such as, "I am weak; I am defective; I am unworthy; I am not good enough." We then set out trying to collect evidence to support the hypothesis. A good scientist would tell you that the purpose of an experiment is not to support or deny the theory but to collect observations and then form conclusions, but because there is an emotional charge behind these hypotheses regarding our own self-worth, we don't go looking for objective data; we are only looking for proof of support. And let's face it; we all want to be right!

Then we go through our lives cataloging information that builds a case. If I am weak, then my inability to do pull-ups in elementary PE class supports that theory, and the bullying that results from peers in that class supports the hypothesis further. So I make an assumption that I am weak; I support it through my action/inability to do pull-ups, and then it is solidified by what is done to me, and I become a victim of bullying. From that point on, every interaction that doesn't go well, every choice that results in failure, and every experience that brings up negativity is further proof. Until finally, the hypothesis is accepted as fact, and it becomes the basis for my life's story. The problem is, it was never true.

Along the course of collecting data, every morsel of evidence to support doubt is noted, and the bits of information that oppose it are sifted through and rejected. There may have been several interactions or experiences that refuted the idea of being unworthy, but we discarded those, not even acknowledging the positive moments and negating compliments all along the way.

He's just saying that to be nice.

That was easy, anyway. Anyone could've done that.

Of course she's going to say that; she's my mother.

Instead, we emphasized the negative, whether it was accurate or not, whether it was substantial or not.

You couldn't even do that right.

Did you notice how they looked at you?

That was stupid!

Every piece of evidence builds a stronger case for the idea that we want to prove. The more convincing the data is, the more it is worth; therefore, while a doubtful mind sifts through every bit of information, it especially notices the big experiences.

In Jay's story, he was already uneasy about his safety, but then his father's deployment anchored his doubts in a much bigger way. It impacted him in such a powerful manner that Jay's three-year-old mind remembered every detail of that difficult day, right down to the specific sights and the intense sensations.

Kate was a forty-two-year-old woman, who'd sought

approval from others all her life. She felt satisfaction through relentless acts of kindness and from being a martyr for those around her. Her needs never took priority, but despite her people-pleasing actions, when her husband left her, it solidified every doubt about her worth.

Seth, a sixteen-year-old young man with a learning disability, had struggled throughout his years of schooling. Not only were academics challenging, but his impulsive behaviors were constantly getting him into trouble, and his anger was escalating. His exhausted and frustrated parents were at their wit's end. Every experience underscored Seth's theory that he would never amount to anything, but none was as powerful in confirming his doubts as the day he failed tenth grade.

Deena should have been excited during her senior year of high school, but instead her obsessive thoughts were getting worse. Her irrational fears were mounting, and if she did not follow them with the compulsion to perform certain rituals, she worried that something would happen to her family. This fear had plagued her thoughts for as long as she could remember, but it heightened after her parents divorced two years ago.

In each of these accounts, fear had made its presence known from a very young age, and then everyday life fed it. The smaller incidents had shaped each person's way of thinking and feeling and had conditioned both body and mind to react, and then the bigger moments cemented these further. The examples go on and on: for Reed, it was a battle with leukemia; for Breanna, it was learning that she had been adopted; for Lacy, it was the horrifying car accident that almost stole her children from her; and for Tad, it was every episode of being teased for his sexuality and his weight.

For me, it was the trauma of abuse.

Your Insights

CHAPTER 11
My Secret Shame

I was sexually abused from the early years of elementary school until I was a teenager by an uncle. I don't remember if I had a lot of specific doubts or fears before it all started, but as I have said, I believe we are all born with a certain temperament; therefore, my anxious filter must have been there all along. I do know I was a pleaser and genuinely wanted others to be happy with me. I also know I took pride in being a rule-follower, especially those rules set by authority figures whom I respected and loved.

While I don't recall all the details of the first encounter or even those of many that followed, I can reflect now on the seduction that was carried out by my perpetrator, and I can understand now, as an adult, why I was an ideal victim. From a child's perspective, though, this was a grown-up in my life whom I trusted and cared about. The seduction began as a game. I believed we were playing, and I certainly had no reason to think otherwise. I don't know how the line was crossed by my uncle that first time, but I clearly recall still having a sense of trust in this man. I didn't say "no," and I didn't fight back, even though undressing with someone in this way felt instinctively wrong and shameful. So when the game ended and I was told to keep our secret, I felt like an accomplice, not a victim.

Over the years, I felt further invested in the seduction. Every time he whispered in my ear when no one was looking, it felt as though we had conspired. In every episode that he orchestrated, I felt like we had gotten away with something. And for every time that he looked excited or satisfied, it felt like we were justified in keeping a secret. His sin morphed into our secret and then rooted my shame.

From that point on, life happened. Among the love of my family and friends, I faced many of the challenges that children do, but through my filter of doubt and saddled with the secret I carried.

Having felt the presence of fear for as long as I could remember, I was terrified to be away from my parents— as a result, the mornings of elementary school were stressful. I wasn't sure at the time what exactly I dreaded happening, but the feeling in my stomach seemed to be warning me of some impending tragedy. I worried that something would happen to me, but I feared even more that something would happen to my parents. What would happen to me if they were gone?

Middle-school years were a mix of stresses and successes. On one hand, I had made some good friends, and through a more rigorous academic challenge than elementary school had offered, I found out more about my potential and just how intoxicating it was for me to be recognized for it. On the other hand, those years were also tainted with the pressures of being bullied.

Developmentally, this is a time when young kids are defining themselves apart from their parents, but unfortunately, they then gauge themselves based on peer feedback, a habit that persists for many into adulthood. And my filter highlighted the judgment of bullies more than the positive interactions that filled my days. There was some physical intimidation, but the hurtful words provided greater damning evidence for the hypothesis that "I wasn't good enough."

The racial slurs, the commentary on my appearance, and the references to being a nerd were all sharp criticisms of my self-worth, but the horrible names that kids used to question another's sexuality were especially harmful. During a time of hormonal surges and heightened sexual awareness, when girls and boys are *liking* and *loving*, I was guarding my secret, and every stabbing word out of a bully's mouth triggered the shame and fueled the fear that the secret had been discovered.

By the time I reached high school, I found that my self-worth was most fortified by my academic successes. Those were the measures that allowed me to thrive among my peers in the most positive light. Every award and accomplishment was validation of what I had to offer, just as a trophy would be for an athlete. Moreover, my performance was a direct result of my efforts, which gave me some measure of control—anxious people like to control every variable possible so that the outcome will be exactly what they envision it to be.

Anxious people like the reassurance that a certain action should lead to a predictable result, which then eliminates the uncomfortable feelings that accompany the unexpected or undesired moments in life. The rude awakening for a fearful person comes from the acknowledgment that not every variable is in his control, and even when he does what is in his control, the result is not always what he hoped for. Rather than accept that, however, he assumes that he must not have done enough or ultimately wasn't good enough. Therefore, I didn't focus on the accolades that I received but chose instead to lament the scholarships that had slipped through my fingers.

In these ways and throughout the different phases in my life, I continued to collect evidence for my false hypothesis until I formed my story, my "truth." I am certain that those closest to me would be surprised to hear it even now, but I had convinced myself that my failures outweighed my successes, and I worried that every recognition I had received was undeserved. Indeed, it was only a matter of time before someone noticed the mistake and would come to take it all back or that I would somehow jinx it all away.

This is also where I took those cultural discussions of karma and made them fit my fear. My interpretation of karma was that if you do bad things, bad things will happen to you. Going back to the notion that I was an accomplice in my own abuse, I judged myself for doing something horribly wrong; therefore, I would feel karma's wrath at any point.

Anxious people are always waiting for the worst to happen. For me, instead of recognizing my dread of the other shoe dropping as a manifestation of anxiety's presence, I believed my intuitive gut was anticipating the inevitable punishment that was my fate. Karma would take its toll; it was only a matter of time. I even took the concept of karma one step further. I must have already done something so bad that I was punished by being abused. After all, why me?

CHAPTER 12

Awaiting Karma's Wrath

Why me? is another one of life's biggest questions repeatedly asked in my office. People want to know what they did to cause or deserve their feelings of depression and anxiety. Parents especially carry their tremendous guilt into the session, and deep down in their guts, they dread finding out that their child's dilemma is due to their poor skills. Perhaps their perceived failings are further evidence for their own lifelong theories of not being good enough. Parents, who can relate to the experiences of their child because they themselves were or are the same way, further compound their guilt with the weighted conclusion that "I did this to my child! He got this from me!"

Family history points to the connections we have to others through our genes, but to a defeated parent, he passed a defect in himself on to his child.

Some patients, on the other hand, are relieved to hear that the basis for their conditions are genetic, physiological, or chemical; in other words, there was nothing they could have done to avert feeling this way. Inevitably, however, genetics is an insufficient answer to someone's crisis of faith. How could God let this happen? Or what did I do to make God punish me this way?

These are the same self-deprecating thoughts that are

expressed by hundreds of patients in my practice. And in the same way that I had filtered out my experiences through my doubtful lens, people describe constructing their stories to confirm their false truths.

It is why siblings who grew up in the same home often have different accounts of their shared upbringing.

It is why friends who were right there with a person may not have been impacted by a seemingly inconsequential moment or discussion.

It is why parents are often shocked that their child interpreted their words in a way that was never intended.

The people in your life were not proving the same hypothesis you were, and they were not collecting the same data you were. They did not have the same lens, and perhaps after a Moment of Insight, you no longer have the same perspective, either.

My own moment on that bus in College introduced the possibility that maybe some of the assumptions I had made were untrue. I then introduced a second hypothesis. I started with the premise that perhaps as a child of God, I had something good within me. I set up my experiment with my Five Gifts as tools and started to go through the same days that I had lived before, but now I was looking to collect a different set of data. Sure enough, the proof was all around me! There was so much of it around that the real truth revealed itself: *I am a Spark of the Divine.*

Why did that Divine truth not instantly replace the doubtful "truth"? Because over a lifetime, I had proven my fear of being insufficient too well. I was too good of a scientist! I had become my story. I was defective, and I was a sinner, so how could I be a *Spark*? I had done bad things; therefore, I was bad. As a child of God, I had sinned; therefore, I was being punished. That had to be the answer to "Why me?" I was a victim of karma's wrath, of God's disapproval. It made perfect sense! Except as a psychiatrist, it really didn't.

In the course of my calling as a psychiatrist, I am blessed to have met so many good people. I have witnessed patients whom I instinctively could see as *Sparks* but who could not see it themselves. I heard the life stories of others, some of which were undoubtedly filled with hardships more difficult than my own, but I never questioned their innate worth. I consoled the tears and counseled the frustrations with reassuring beliefs that there was purpose even in suffering. I came to see that, through balance and a focus inward, even children had an unlimited capacity to endure and evolve. As a witness to such goodness in my office, I extended my gaze to the plight of the world around me and charged myself to recognize that same goodness beyond my four walls. Time after time, I saw it, and often it pierced through tragedy.

One such example occurred on June 17, 2015. A mass shooting took place at Emanuel African Methodist Episcopal Church in Charleston, South Carolina. During a prayer service, a gunman massacred nine people and injured a tenth. As I watched the media coverage of this senseless tragedy, I wondered, like so many others: How could something like this happen? How could a place of worship be the site of such hatred? What had these poor souls done to be the victims of such violence?

Yet, in the course of my practice, I had witnessed repeatedly that through hardship came the possibility for tremendous change. Sure enough, in the following days, statewide policy was amended, and a national discussion was ignited.

As an animated thinker, trying to sort through it all, I imagined a story that helped me come to terms with this and other difficult times. I imagined the "Cosmic Coffeehouse."

CHAPTER 13

The Cosmic Coffeehouse

I imagined my higher self—not Suvrat Bhargave, but the spirit that is really me—excitedly meeting up with other soul friends at some cosmic coffeehouse in the heavens. Much like frenzied students gather with all of their books to study in a group, my soulful pod was joyfully giddy to meet at this site where we were going to map out the potential pathways for the lives we would all take on together. We were enthusiastic with the prospect of advancing our spiritual and soulful understandings through these possible experiences. The gathering's only intention was our collective betterment; we were motivated only by our entire group advancing. Above all else, the overwhelming sensation and driving force filling the space was pure love, a kind of love that could never be contained in an earthly realm.

As relationships and events were thoughtfully but enthusiastically being devised, the algorithms became incredibly detailed and intricate. After all, the stories were not linear and were not set in stone. They were ripe with possibility and shaped at every turn by the freedom of choice and the force of will. If this choice was made, then this could potentially happen, or if this was done instead, then the alternative could be this.

These complicated layers of possibilities would become a complex contract between souls.

Again, the goal was soulful advancement, and the underlying sentiment was utmost love. In the midst of this beautiful exercise, one of the souls spoke up in a more serious tone. This higher being realized there were certain lessons that may only come through adversity and hardship, and again through an abundance of love, that gracious and generous soul then comfortingly declared, "I'm going to take this one." As the rest of the gathering looked around, wanting to deny the harshness of what had to be done and to spare the suffering of someone so cherished, the greater intention again became thoroughly clear. Betterment and love.

The group jointly comforted itself, offered sentiment that is even hard to conceptualize through our human expressions, and then the momentum started to build again. One by one, the souls began to build on the sacrifice of their soul friend, and there was a knowing that, through that person's experience, there could be so many ripple-effect insights gained by several others. While they had surrendered to the need for this act, there was a determination to honor the sacrifice—again, through love.

Those nine souls in that South Carolina church made a sacrifice, and in a ripple-like effect, their act was meant to be transformative and honored—but only if we made the choice to do so. The biggest tragedies we have faced as a nation, or as a community, or as a family have had the greatest potential to bring about collective progression—but only through individual effort to gain insight. Similarly, each occasion of suffering that a single person experiences in the course of this lifetime is meant to be a crossroads for evolution—but only through the awareness of the possibility. Life happens but not without purpose. In this way, every dilemma may best serve if thought of as an opportunity.

I believe that our higher selves in that cosmic coffeehouse chose the lives that we were born into, a notion that I have gradually accepted over time, because when taken at face value, the idea doesn't make sense at first. After all, who would choose dysfunction? Or loss? Or hurt? Or suffering? When given a choice, wouldn't we all pick the perfect household? But I do now believe that if we are meant to learn lessons in this lifetime, then there are reasons why we enter this world when and where we do.

I didn't choose to be molested. I did choose to enter into a contract with the soul that would be my uncle in this lifetime, which set up the expansive algorithm that could be our lives. I did choose to embark on a mutual journey that had the potential for both of us to soulfully advance through interactions and lessons learned. My higher self's singular mission out of pure and Divine love was to create a lifetime filled with purpose—not necessarily filled with guaranteed constant happiness, but through intricate design, my pathway would overlap with many, including my uncle, and if choices were made and if will was exerted, we could all meet back at that cosmic cafe and rejoice in a heavenly celebration of lives well-lived.

I didn't choose to be molested. My uncle chose to molest me. And in doing so, the algorithm shifted. It didn't alter it to a forgone outcome, but it set up the next opportunity, which could then lead to the next, and so forth. Karma to me is about balance. If my decision had a negative impact away from my soul's purpose, then there must be a way of understanding it and of restoring balance. While every decision has the potential to carry me further away from my soul's purpose, the good news is that every choice can set up a cascade of events to carry me back toward my soul's purpose. I also believe that my end of every contract with other souls is satisfied when I learn the lesson that my higher self intended, whether or not the other soul did the same. Each time I choose to do so, I am empowered, and I am no longer a victim.

So, back to that cosmic coffeehouse. Among all of those higher beings who so excitedly gathered for our betterment, there was another presence to oversee it all. Throughout the exercise was the underlying presence of love. When that soul assumed his sacrifice, the force that comforted the collective was love. When all of those pathways and algorithms were finally devised, they were all sealed with love.

When a decision is made in a lifetime that deviates a soul from its purpose, the energy that hopes to guide it back on track is love. And when an opportunity is realized, the presence that unabashedly and limitlessly rejoices and celebrates is love.

God is love, and for every step that I take toward my soul's purpose, He does cartwheels in that cafe.

CHAPTER 14

One Fish, Two Fish

How can I let it go?

"One fish, two fish, red fish ..." One of my most cherished memories from when my children were little was the joy in reading to them. I could see the excitement in their eyes as they grabbed a book and then cozied into a loving snuggle, anticipating the first page. I could barely fit in the words, "One fish, two fish, red fish," before one or both of them triumphantly exclaimed, "Blue fish!" This was followed by a hurried motion to turn the page. Their familiarity with this book meant that the illustrations were quickly glanced over, and, instead, they would impatiently shake over the best parts still to come. They knew the story. I knew the story. Yet the magic of Dr. Seuss inspired my children to be just as thrilled for the hundredth reading as they had been for the first. And just as I had raced to read the first full page, I would scarcely utter the last word of the last page, when they would plead, "Again!" The memory is cherished now, but the moment at that time was rather tiring. The same story over and over and over.

That's how we are with our own life stories. We start with an idea and then orchestrate an intricate narrative that gets told in our heads over and over again. And the author of that story is the child within us. We allow that inner child, who introduced a theory—based on some life experience or some innate sense of doubt—to outline the rest of our lives. If a six-year-old entered the room right now and declared that he had life figured out and that he would, therefore, be running things from now on, would we hand him the keys? But in the course of practicing psychiatry, that's exactly what I have witnessed most people having done.

They took the theory of that wounded, scared, defeated, or angry child and proved it into *fact*. They've constructed chapters by picking up evidence along the course of their lives and made sure that it fit the outline of their inner child. They've conditioned themselves to respond so quickly to the familiar narrative that they can hardly take in the full picture before they have already turned the page. They have scarcely uttered, "Once upon a time," before they have already envisioned the conclusion, and unfortunately, it isn't a happily-ever-after ending.

I have, however, also witnessed countless Moments of Insight when the story is challenged. Over the course of sessions, I have watched patients introduce a new narrative, with the perspective of someone who is no longer a child. The challenge is to take that Moment of Insight and expand on it. And that is a very difficult task when the story we are starting to write is competing with the novel we have read to ourselves repeatedly. We've conditioned ourselves to respond one way, "One fish, two fish, red fish, blue fish" for so long. The thinking becomes so second-nature that we confuse it with an innate instinct: "I can't help it!" And even when we experience a moment in which we see that we have proven a false "fact" all of our lives, we are drawn back into unhealthy thinking. This is when people start asking, "How can I let go?"

If we have trained our minds one way, the glorious fact is that we can also train them to think in another. It isn't easy, but conditioning never is. If someone were to pull me off my comfy chair right now, drag me outside, and challenge me to run a marathon, I guarantee that I couldn't do it. But they tell me (the "they" in this case being all those dedicated athletes whom I see jogging outside in the cold from my view here inside as I sit on my comfy chair) that if I began training now, I could certainly run a marathon in six months. I may begin by taking long walks and then increase to a more brisk pace. Perhaps I would then walk/jog/walk to build my endurance further. With determination, practice, and, yes, discomfort, I would eventually be able to achieve my goal with exhilaration. Reconditioning our way of thinking is most certainly a marathon.

The process of letting go is two-pronged. It requires the building up of a second narrative that will eventually replace the first. At the same time, it requires deconstructing the original false storyline. For me, that day at college when I had my Moment of Insight introduced the second storyline of my life: *I am a creation or a child of God, and God resides within me.* The chapters grew from there: *as His creation, I must have innate gifts,* and once I knew what those were, I recognized that they shouldn't be wasted. Until finally, the last page of that book revealed: *I am a Spark of the Divine.* The duality of letting go would now require my telling this story to myself over and over again, while chipping away at the previous story that I had committed to memory as truth. I would build the narrative of innate self-worth, while questioning the familiar story of not being good enough.

The process of letting go requires awareness and commitment. It means catching yourself in the habit of your negative dialogue. It means resisting the familiar urge to feed it. It means questioning the validity of every piece of evidence that made that original theory seem true. It means choosing to substitute your new story, even if it doesn't feel completely truthful or comfortable just yet. And it means repeating these steps over and over again.

Your original story—the one that your Moment of Insight revealed as having been unhealthy for you—started in childhood and persisted over all of these years. Therefore, letting go will take time. But much like a marathon, the hard work will pay off.

CHAPTER 15

Constructing a New Life Narrative

Nadia, a thirty-something-year-old who first came to see me years ago, would tell you that her work of letting go has been worthwhile. She had experienced bouts of depression for most of her life, but when she had reached out to make that initial appointment with me, Nadia was desperate. A divorced mother of two children, she described a worsening sense of emptiness, and she knew her life was critically falling apart. Her job in retail had never been satisfying, but it had served to pay her bills; now she had been warned that her position was in jeopardy due to her carelessness and lack of enthusiasm toward customers.

At home, her relationships with most of the people in her life were suffering. Her ex-husband, who had remarried and "happily moved on," had successfully petitioned the courts to reconsider custody of their children—both were now primarily living at his house. The worst part of the legal process had been her sixteen-year-old son's declaration that he wanted to live with his father. His preference wasn't surprising, given their contentious and worsening interactions, but it had still been hurtful. What had made it even more so was the condemnation of Nadia's own mother, who had been critical of her throughout her life and had "predicted that this would happen." Her eleven-year-old daughter continued to be affectionate and supportive, but Nadia could see that her caretaking child was becoming more and more anxious as Nadia herself became more obviously debilitated by her symptoms. Her daughter's well-being during one particular interaction was the impetus for Nadia's Moment of Insight.

Nadia had often considered that both of her children would have been better off without her. Her passive desire for an end had transformed into more active thoughts of suicide. She had convinced herself that while her daughter would be sad initially, she would eventually move on and, over time, thrive. This train of rationalization came to an abrupt halt at the end of a weekend visit with her child. As her daughter hugged her goodbye, the girl uttered, "I won't let anything happen to you."

Her child had often worried about something happening to her family members, but this was the first time that she had taken ownership of their care: "I won't let anything happen." In that Moment, as Nadia would later explain to me in one of our sessions, "I saw my whole life play out in front of me."

Nadia grew up as the middle child of an alcoholic father and a stay-at-home mother. Her older sister was known for her "independent spirit," which resulted in frequent clashes with their parents. Nadia described home as a scene for ongoing battles and school as a refuge for temporary peace. She acknowledged that her fear of further conflict made her stay more to herself so that most of her peers would have described her as the "shy one" or "the loner." Her younger sister, on the other hand, reacted to the turmoil at home by disengaging from the family; she was "the social one," who balanced the demands of a large circle of friends, a different sport for every season, and academic achievement in accelerated classes. The younger sister always had a reason to be out of the home, and the older one would sneak out and inevitably return (or be brought back) in trouble.

If her older sibling was the troublemaker, then Nadia was the peacekeeper. And because the majority of the clashes involved her father, she worked extra hard to keep him happy. Nadia recognized, however, that being Daddy's Girl came at the cost of her relationship with her mom. Through the thin wall between the room Nadia shared with her younger sister and the master bedroom, she would often hear her parents arguing. Her sister seemingly slept through it all, but Nadia found herself resenting her mother more with every fight. Why couldn't she let him be? Did she enjoy being a nag? After all that she had done to maintain the balance and to reverse the damage that her sister had caused, her mother couldn't wait to corner her father and undo it all. All that walking on eggshells ... wasted!

Nadia suspected that the resentment she felt toward her mother was mutual. Everyone in the family knew that if her father was upset, Nadia was the only one who could calm him down. She could count the handful of times that she had witnessed her parents being affectionate toward one another, but she herself cherished her father's bear hugs. She felt his love through every gesture, knew how hard he worked to provide for them, and relied on his strong presence through every hurdle in her life. So, when he died, the grief triggered one of her worst episodes of depression. Nadia would later recall that she had contemplated suicide at that point as well, but these thoughts were more fleeting and seemed to resolve shortly after she met the man who would become her husband.

Nadia acknowledged that prior to their separation, she would have told the story of their courtship in more romantic terms, but the truth is, her ex-husband had never been very affectionate. He did give her attention, though, and he had always provided well for their family. She met him in the year of her father's abrupt passing, and much to her surprise, this relationship was one of the few times that she remembered getting her mother's approval. In fact, her mom's admiration for this man overtook any allegiance between parent and daughter. She would declare her gratitude for his "taking on" Nadia and praised his "principled" approach to being a husband. In contrast, she always had plenty of advice for Nadia on how to keep him happy and how to raise their children. Even when her husband's affairs were revealed, Nadia was criticized for not nurturing the marriage enough. The irony of her mother's feedback irritated Nadia most of all. Where did this woman, who had made her own husband miserable and who could not control her own daughter's rebellious behaviors, get the right to instruct her?

Nadia's intention was to become the mother that she had dreamed of having. She would offer praise freely and pick her battles cautiously. Her goal was to spare them disappointment and minimize conflict in their lives. Nadia wanted to make sure that her children had activities to entertain and opportunities to enjoy.

Over time, she could feel the weight of her own desperation. Nothing was ever good enough, immediate enough, or valuable enough for her kids. Her unreasonable expectations and frenzied advocacy for her children had cost her friendships, taken a toll on her marriage, and even affected the children for whom she had been striving. Her son had become increasingly oppositional, and Nadia found herself reacting to him in extremes. She either felt the pressure to placate his demands, or she would express anger that was disproportionate to his entitlement. How could he not see that everything she did was for him?

While her son may not have understood, she was grateful that her daughter did. She was an endearing child, who was accommodating and appreciative. She was gentle and always looking out for others. It was this same level of empathy, though, which also fed the girl's fears.

Nadia's daughter worried beyond her years. She was irrationally scared for their health, their finances, and, most of all, their safety. Every night was a ritual of reassurance that every precaution had been made to keep their home safe, and every morning was a routine of providing comfort that they would all be safely back together again soon. For the child's entire life, Nadia had reassured her that she was safe, until that Sunday afternoon when her daughter turned the tables and proclaimed, "I won't let anything happen to you."

The comment had caught Nadia so off guard that she didn't respond to her child. She simply hugged her back tightly and then watched as the little girl rode away with her father. Then, Nadia sank to the ground and wept. She was struck with the realization that if she were to remove herself from her daughter's life, her child would take ownership of that as well. She wouldn't just "get over" her mother's death; she would take responsibility for it.

Nadia regretted not telling her daughter right then that she needn't worry about her. She wanted to call and reassure her child that, as the parent, she would take care of herself. She wanted to relieve her child's burden and make it clear that no eleven-year-old could take on that kind of responsibility. No child could be the reason for another's well-being. No little girl could ensure what was not hers to control.

No little girl could.

There was the Moment of Insight! Nadia had done exactly that! The child within her had taken ownership of factors that were not hers to control.

She couldn't keep her sister from being rebellious.

She couldn't ensure her father's happiness or anyone else's.

She couldn't stop him from drinking.

She couldn't prevent them from arguing.

She couldn't make her husband love her in the way that she wanted.

She couldn't shield her children from disappointment.

But the little girl who had believed that she was responsible for the complete well-being of everyone in her life had set the premise for the story. And every moment where it seemed true and every instance where she had failed to do so were woven into the narrative. The impossibility of the storyline gave way to the "truth" that her worth was tied to the outcomes and opinions of others.

Her moment, however, introduced the second story of her life. While she wasn't even sure how that novel might read, she knew instinctively that it needed to start with her taking responsibility for her own happiness, and she needed to let go of the control that she had tried to have over the actions and attitudes of others.

And so began our journey together.

———••———

For Nadia, being responsible for her own happiness first meant addressing her depression. She had read enough and heard enough about depression to understand that she needed professional help. She had thought of doing so many times before but would either rationalize not needing it or shame herself into avoiding it. The depression itself had drained her of any motivation to act, while her anxiety had cemented her fear of being judged if she were to let anyone know how she had been feeling. As most patients do, she entered my office on that first appointment burdened with shame, and she left with the relief that accompanies safe disclosure.

Once Nadia's depression started to improve, she began the difficult task of mending her soul. She needed the premise of her second story. Her Moment of Insight had challenged the notion that her worth was exclusively tied to her actions and to their effects on the people in her life. So instead, she began with the basic hypothesis: "I am worthy ... simply because I am."

She struggled to even say it at first. She herself had formulated the premise of the statement, but Nadia had a hard time saying it out loud two minutes after proposing it. I believe that the divinity of her soul had seen an opportunity to shine through, which is what brought the idea to her lips, but her own humanity stepped back in and reminded her to doubt. With a little more encouragement, though, she began to explore the concept further. She could accept that she had been given life. She didn't just happen to fall onto the earth. She didn't somehow sneak past God. So then, perhaps she was worthy, simply for having been created.

For many months after that, she built on that idea. She found that the more she looked, the more data she found to develop this story further. She read books which she had rejected before, when she had only been looking for evidence that she wasn't good enough. She noticed her own interactions with others through a clearer filter, thereby giving herself credit for the many exchanges which were pleasant rather than tallying the few that weren't. She more thoughtfully chose the people that she hung around, seeking conversations that were fortifying and trusted rather than judgmental and negative.

Session after session, Nadia brought more of the evidence that she had collected. Actions that she had undertaken simply out of empathy and good intention. Talents that came easily to her. Skills that she had worked hard to acquire. Mistakes that she had made but learned from and not repeated. And moments in her day when she felt at ease just in the presence of her own company. All of these examples built on that idea that she was worthy simply for being.

As Nadia became more comfortable with the possibility of her second hypothesis, she was ready to begin challenging the previous story, which the child within her had authored. As much as she had improved on balancing her sense of self, the conviction of her unworthiness over all those years was a tough habit to break. But much like the breaking of any other habit, the first step would be the awareness of the habit. (When pointed out, a nail-biter will often respond that he wasn't even aware of doing it in that moment.)

She accepted my suggestion that she should first become an observer to her own thoughts. Nadia's criticism of herself had become so instinctual that she didn't even know how consumed her inner voice had become with tearing herself down. She needed to call herself out just as soon as she became aware of the old pattern. But in calling herself out, I didn't want her to compound her own criticism: *There you go doing it again; you really are a lost cause.*

Instead, as an observer, she was instructed to objectively collect data, to notice the pattern but without judgment. Eventually she would learn to give herself credit for catching the old pattern of thinking and even mentally pat herself on the back for it. We had talked about the Dr. Seuss phenomenon of retelling our tales, so each time she caught herself, she would simply chuckle in her mind: *blue fish.* That became her mantra for noticing those familiar imposing thoughts and for lovingly nudging herself to not feed them further. After all, what's the point of deconstructing the story on one hand, if you are going to keep feeding it with the other?

Deconstructing a story means that you must next challenge the pieces of that narrative which had convinced you of its "truth." You have to reexamine the data that had proven the initial hypothesis. Either it was skewed, or your interpretation of it was flawed. In this way, Nadia began looking back on the circumstances and situations in her life which had fed her fear of letting others down.

The first time that Nadia had talked about her father in one of our sessions, she had referred to him as her "biggest supporter," and he certainly had been. Just as he had undoubtedly loved her. But in an effort to analyze the relationship objectively, Nadia could acknowledge that she needed his validation much like an addict needs a hit. And he was a reliable supplier of what she lacked. In a moment when she felt inadequate, she could count on his responding to her gestures of comfort and consolation. However, if Nadia relied on his validation, the truth is, her father also needed hers. Despite the many consequences that his drinking had placed on the family, and regardless of what his motivations were to continue doing so despite them, Nadia's affection for her father was his respite from those burdens. Much like the addiction itself was likely a temporary respite from his own sense of unworthiness. In Nadia's childhood story, she needed him to be the hero, which meant editing the reality of his behaviors. Similarly, for a man who felt anything but heroic within his own private narrative, he readily accepted the role, despite what his experience, or his wife, told him.

If a story needs a hero, then it also needs a villain. Over the course of many sessions, Nadia had used several phrases to describe her mother, and all of them emphasized her antagonizing place in her life. Nadia had said more than once that she could not remember a time when she didn't feel conflicted in their relationship. Despite her efforts to please, Nadia commented that her mother wouldn't respond like her father did.

There was another Moment of Insight! On some level, she *needed* her mother to not respond the way her father would. In that way, his reactions were highlighted with greater value, and when he didn't respond as she had hoped, Nadia could attribute his inadequacies to her mother being a nag. For one parent to be the hero despite his flaws, she relied on her nemesis to be flawed beyond redemption.

Through careful and objective reflection, Nadia came to realize that she had sifted through the evidence around her to support the story which had fed her fear of unworthiness. There was no doubt her mother had provided plenty of fodder through her relentless criticism (Nadia could later theorize that the habit of doing so may have been partly due to her mother's own sense of frustration and inadequacy) but there were also a few memories of her mother's love, appreciation, and support. And more importantly, if her mother's criticisms were really just a reflection of what Nadia had convinced herself of internally, then her mother's efforts to comfort her would never have been received with sincere appreciation anyway.

Nadia continued to deconstruct her story by reexamining each character in her life. Her older sister's troublemaking ways were the perfect foil for Nadia's talents to please. She had resented her sibling's rebellion, but it had also taken the negative spotlight, which Nadia had dreaded and perceived having, off of her. Her ex-husband would be the replacement hero for her loss of her father, and with that same template of a relationship, she edited his flaws during the foundation phase of their union so that he could take on the role of supplier for the hits that her addiction to reassurance required. And by the time she could no longer deny his challenges and their incompatibility, Nadia's role as mother became the venue for validating her worth. But much like trying to fill a bottomless pit, the void within her sparked a desperation that no mother could, nor should, feel the pressure to satisfy. Until finally, the dissolution of her marriage and the rejection of her son marked the finale of the tragedy which was her life.

It has been a few years now since Nadia first walked through my door. She has balanced her efforts between deconstructing the previous story that she had recited over and over again and building the next narrative of her life. She has experienced setbacks along the way, and she is still reconciling some of the relationships within her family. She has even accepted that a few are beyond mending, or they are hindered by the resistance of the other person involved, which she cannot control. But with each passing day, the "truth" that the child within her had proven fades a bit at a time. The dread that she had felt at the start or end of her day has been gradually replaced by a Divine sense of reassurance.

The dawn of a new day brings fluctuating possibility, but there is a sacred truth that is constant. There is nothing that she, or you, could do, think, or say that would result in the Divinity within each of us being diminished. Just as there is nothing more to do, think, or say which could garnish any more favor. For she, just like you, is a Spark which survives all shade and a Reflection that could not be any more beautiful. Knowing that, just imagine the possibility.

Your Insights

CHAPTER 16

Sweep It Under the Rug

How do I make my suffering stop?

Many patients over the years have commented on the weight of the baggage that they carry, which in itself is a powerful Moment of Insight: *I am unable to move forward because of the past.* However, acknowledging the burden of these weights doesn't by itself relieve you of their impact. You have to unpack each bag and put it in its place, once and for all. Counseling can assist in that process. Therapy is meant to look for patterns of thinking, feeling, or behaving that are not working, to understand where they may have originated, and then to challenge the patterns by creating new ones. Patients in counseling seek to live today better, despite their troubled pasts or despite their apprehensions about the future. That goal in itself is a spiritual endeavor. After all, every enlightened being and every evolved teacher reminds us to live a more "present" life. We are advised to be in the "now" and to practice being mindful. Until past anchors are released, though, you can't be completely present.

Counseling is a thoughtful process for releasing past experiences step by step, much like meditation is the gradual progression of training your active, chattering mind to settle down to a place of silent, soulful connection in the now. There are times, however, when unreleased emotion barges through, like an anchor that suddenly snaps you back with the worst case of whiplash. These are the times when your reaction to a current frustration is out of proportion to whatever brought it on, so much so that you find yourself pondering, "Where did that come from?" These reactions are opportunities to understand what unresolved or unreleased emotions are demanding to be set free. The reflection requires vulnerability and honesty, but if the opportunity is seized, you can find yourself one step closer to being done with your past and to being freed from your story.

Deconstructing our stories means not just challenging the thoughts that accompany our memories but also the emotions attached to them. We not only retell our stories in our heads, but we *feel* them repeatedly. Within the safe space of my office, patients have relayed countless stories of pain: the loss of a loved one, the course of a fatal diagnosis, the act of betrayal, the consequence of hurting others, the trauma of abuse, the stress of "not having." So many circumstances and moments of tragedy. But the greatest displays of courage I have witnessed have not been in the telling of these stories; they have been in the rawness of re-experiencing them during a vulnerable session. And while individual stories are unique, the feelings that accompany these dilemmas are shared by every one of us. What have you felt that I haven't? Therefore, it ought to be that if you share your story with another in a vulnerable way, the listener will be able to understand some of how you felt or feel, even if they have not experienced the trauma that hurt you. If pain can be defined as the hurt that results from an action, then suffering is the repeated emotional response we have to those times of pain. And we have all replayed traumas from the past and felt our responses to these again, as if a wound had been reopened. It is this repeated expression of powerful feelings that results in patients seeking comfort and wanting to know, "How do I make my suffering stop?"

As we experience challenges in our lives, we feel a wide range of emotions, including sadness, disappointment, fear, and anger. For every circumstance that caused hurt, we naturally hope to shield ourselves from feeling that type of pain again. The instinct is understandable; if you have ever burned your hand, you would like to avoid potential fires going forward. And when a stressful situation that feels vaguely familiar presents itself, our instinct is to get through the moment quickly, to lay feelings aside if possible, or to escape in some way without having to feel discomfort. When we fall down, our quick reaction is to get right back up, brush ourselves off, and hope that no one witnessed it. Emotionally, we tend to do the same. Rather than allowing ourselves to feel completely, we are quick to distract ourselves. Emotional deferment, however, has a bad habit of coming out later when we least expect it, and in a disproportionate way.

All emotions demand release. But when we buffer

ourselves, we tether our souls. We anchor ourselves with the weight of unreleased emotion. We do this multiple times, until the collective burden can no longer be denied, and the emotions come rushing through.

The biggest anchors that impede us are the ones rooted in our childhood stories. Not only did your inner child hold on to your experiences, but you also held on to the emotions that went along with them. Very few children have the capacity to identify and express feelings accurately, but you did the best you could and then instinctively tried to make those difficult emotions go away so you could feel better. In doing so, you unintentionally anchored part of your spirit to that misunderstood and unreleased experience, and as anchors tend to do, these cumulative weights held you back. Imagine that the older the anchor is, the heavier it has become, and the longer it takes to release that kind of burden.

---••---

My Heavy Anchor

For me, the tether that has been the most difficult to sever is rooted in my childhood abuse. Very few experiences in life feed the lie of shame in the way that sexual molestation does. And it speaks to the power of shame that it would make a child, who otherwise knew the security and joy of a loving household, keep such a big violation secret. But I did so, even when it happened repeatedly. There were many reasons, which an adult may or may not understand. However, the greatest urges pushing for secrecy were not the rational ones; they were the emotional ones. Every emotion tied to every episode was uncomfortable. Therefore, in an effort to not be overwhelmed and in an instinct to survive, I felt my trauma in doses and then boxed the rest away. My emotional deferment was necessary; most adults wouldn't have the tools to deal with it all, much less a child. So, the only way to process the range of emotions involved was to measure it a little at a time until I no longer felt that I could. I didn't consciously devise the plan at the time, but I do understand it now. And I also understand that to keep this process going, I had become very invested in no one finding out. I succeeded in doing this for many, many years.

The first person I told was my wife Kali. I will never forget the moment I did so, even though the details leading up to it escape me. It was in the earlier stages of our marriage, and the admission had not been planned. What I do remember, and all that mattered, was her reaction. I could tell that Kali felt immense sadness as she cried. I knew that beyond the shock of what I had just revealed, she wanted so badly to make me feel better. Indeed, as she hugged me tightly and allowed me to sob against her, I felt powerfully loved, and the child inside that had held on to a terrible secret for so long felt assuredly protected. I can only describe it now as a complete letting go. Physically, I could collapse against her and exhale fully, and for the moment at least, my soul expanded in a way that I couldn't have anticipated. I will never be able to convey my gratitude to this woman. Kali was everything that I needed her to be in that moment, and so much more than I ever could have imagined needing.

Then came her anger. Not toward me but toward the man who had done this to me. Part of what had initially attracted me to and intimidated me about this impressive woman who became my wife was her unrelenting strength and determination. I say that it had been intimidating because, in the process of our courtship, I saw her duality: this undeniably beautiful and caring young lady also had the armor of a warrior. Would I be able to get through the armor, or would I be on the receiving end of it? Now, twenty-five years later, I am grateful to say that the warrior found the courage to be vulnerable, and as a result of that mutually courageous choice, we have the gift of a Divine and soulful connection.

Despite the moments of intimidation, her strength has been a quality to admire. In the countless ways I have seen her strength manifest during our marriage, sometimes through quiet assurance and other times through outward fierceness, where I have seen it unleashed most boldly is in defense of the ones whom she loves the most. Make a threat toward one of her cubs and watch what a mama bear can do! So when Kali described the anger that she felt toward my perpetrator, I drew from her energy. I also rejoiced in her wanting to beat this person up! *Yes! Let's knock this bastard down!*

Over the years, I have continued to be fortified in her strength and have seen her anger reflect the intense hatred that I felt during my childhood and young adult life for my abuser. For me in my later adulthood, there is anger in moments of reflection, but usually it is summoned rather than triggered. Or so I thought.

Yes, if I sit with the hurt child inside of me, I feel animosity, much as my wife felt in that first comforting embrace of protection. There was so much more for my grown-up self to tell that child and so many more feelings to be shared between me and my child self—I assumed my anger had been mostly released. But I learned during an episode many years later that I had not completely let go of my suffering.

My Trigger: More Work to Do

There have been times during our marriage that my wife's frustration was directed toward me, specifically my choice to not say anything about my abuse to anyone. Kali has listened and understood my reasons. She has been respectful of them as well; however, she has intermittently encouraged me to speak my truth. She has wondered out loud how I could restrain myself around my abuser, whom I would see on occasions through family gatherings. She is one to speak her mind, so her opinions on this subject have been openly expressed between us, but her intentions were abundantly clear and always in my best interest. Those were never the moments that hurt. The ones that stung were the short phrases that escaped during arguments and the ones that I can now honestly recognize as being triggers for me beyond the context of when they were used.

One of those raw nerves was exposed during an argument whose details are completely lost to me because of the irrelevance of these small matters in the big picture of a relationship, but in pointing out to me a pattern of reaction within my family, Kali described us "sweeping things under the rug." I can't even now comprehend the rush that came over me. I felt my lip quiver as my insides shook, my thoughts exploded in eerie silence, and my anger crescendoed in a scream that more resembled a growl. Without any other words to cypher through my rushed barrage of thoughts, feelings, and sensations, I uttered, "Don't you dare!" I slammed the door, ran out of the house, and briskly walked a path into the woods. In the eye of the hurricane of my own reactions, I watched a part of me wanting to stay angry with Kali, while another remorsefully pleading to turn back, and yet another part fearing my own anger.

I knew quickly that my trigger had little to do with what had led up to it, and I felt awful about the intense reaction that I had directed toward my wife. My partner had not deserved an exponential explosion of anger that went beyond whatever we were dealing with in that mutually frustrating argument. The lesson that needed my attention was to understand the root of my trigger.

This dilemma could become the opportunity to put my

finger on the tether from my past which was being snapped back into my present. There was a clarity in knowing that, without understanding the trigger, the abscessed wound to my soul would spew forth once again when pricked somewhere else in the future. The person on the receiving end of that next triggered moment would no more deserve that than Kali had in the above example … and my next realization was that I didn't deserve that, either. I deserved the right to be totally present. If previous triggers were worked on and released, I could be more mindful of what was being experienced now. Without the weight of extra baggage, I could be free to *just be*. Whether that meant being happy, sad, angry, worried, embarrassed, or confused in any given moment, I owed it to myself to release this anchor.

I reminded myself of the advice that I had offered so many patients over the years: identify all that you are feeling, sit with each emotion in its own space, and then follow the natural flow of the emotion demanding to be released. Through this meditative process of acknowledging and allowing emotion to come forth, I could eventually alleviate my suffering. So, I took several deep breaths, found my thoughts settling down, and then began the process of release.

Sweep it under the rug. What feelings had that phrase triggered?

The first emotion that I felt was helpless—because my years-long investment in keeping this secret divided and packaged had been exposed. And not just exposed, but seen as an act of weakness, as an attempt to hide something in order to not deal with it. Helplessness is inherently bound to victimhood. Whether an assault is countered by kicking and screaming or it is committed in the cloak of silence, a victim is stripped of choice. And as a result of someone else's actions, life is altered in one of the most profound ways possible. And for me, the transgressions had occurred in my home, my place of safe refuge that had been fortified by the love of so many family members. And yet it was a family member, my uncle, who had made the choices within my home that would change my life. He had not only violated me physically, but he had taken from me my sense of security. So, yes, part of the sting from my wife's statement so many years later came from feeling vulnerable and helpless all over again.

As I allowed the feeling of helplessness to step forward, I could see how this emotion was tethered and boxed away in so many other examples throughout my life. For every time that my physicality was questioned, I felt helpless and weak. All those times during PE class or when my friends would gather to play outside, I felt weak. Every time my lack of athletic ability or interest was abundantly clear, I felt helpless. Every instance of rejection solidified the false truth of not being good enough. The dread of doing pull-ups in front of peers, the comparison of my body to the build of others when dressing out, the forgone conclusion that I would be the last to be picked for any team. While each of these

A Moment of Insight

examples was annoying and embarrassing enough on its own, what I could now acknowledge was that it added a layer of weight to an already existing anchor.

And those were just the examples of physical defeats that built the case for being helpless. The emotional moments of "proof" were even more numerous. As a kid, I was the poster child for being bullied—what bullies count on is to induce the feeling of weakness and helplessness in others. In order to falsely elevate themselves on the hierarchy among peers, bullies will target any perceived flaw in another. In doing so, the rush of domination camouflages their own actual insecurity. The action of a bully truly does say more about what the bully feels he is lacking, but the toll on the victim is intimidation and self-doubt. The consequence of any single act of bullying is much more powerful than the incident itself. The lingering effect is that it has the potential to feed a false truth of not being good enough or of being weak. And the worst part of being repeatedly victimized over time is that a victim starts to believe what a bully says, or, even more powerfully, he starts to believe that he deserves to be bullied.

So, as I welcomed helplessness to step forward into my present, I allowed myself to feel this same sensation in the moments from the past.

Sweep it under the rug. What else had this triggered?

Anger. The paradoxical reaction to repeated helplessness is intense anger. After feeling unable to act over and over again, victims turn to the emotion that is all about acting out. Whereas other emotions on the spectrum require sitting with the feeling, anger seemingly inspires action, whether it means punching a pillow, shoving a person, throwing an object, or destroying your surroundings. In my case, the perceived verbal jab thrown by Kali was countered with my own growl and subsequent slamming of a door.

As I sat in the woods that day and allowed anger its moment, I could feel the past tethers resonating within me. I really thought I had released my anger regarding my abuse, and the truth was, over time I had, but what I needed to acknowledge was that there were still layers that needed release. The older the anchor, the heavier it gets, and the more work it would require to be released.

Sweep it under the rug. So, what had the phrase *specifically* triggered?

As I have said before, a victim is robbed of choice. I had not chosen my abuse. My uncle chose to taint my childhood through his actions. He had burdened a child with the complexity of emotional entanglement that even adults have the biggest challenges navigating through and figuring out. How does a child reconcile all the feelings that accompany these acts? And without the guidance of adult perspective, the child is left to sort through these in the only way that he can. He is limited but doesn't know it. His conclusions are false, but he has no reason to doubt them. And while the overwhelming emotional consequence is being continually dealt with, the added burden was the weight of a secret.

The word itself is heavy and implies negativity: *secret*. Whereas "surprise" is filled with anticipation of something exciting and fun, "secret" is meant to be hush-hush. And for a child keeping a secret, exposing oneself is terrifying. As a psychiatrist who has the life experiences and perspectives of an adult, I have offered words of reassurance to many patients that what happened was not the child's fault, and I believe that to be undeniably true, but the kid in me has doubted that statement during trying times. From a boy's point of view (and one who is a people pleaser and with an anxious temperament) there is so much blame to be shared, and the perpetrator is invested in strengthening that false notion. Forget where it started. The secret was held between the two of us; therefore, the blame must be shared by the two of us as well. Every incident that was kept from my parents added another layer to my deception.

One of the very first lessons we are taught is the sin of lying. Keeping a secret is a form of lying. At the very least, my child self knew that I was definitely not being truthful. In some ways, the simplicity of a child's diagram of life is refreshing; grownups rationalize decisions all the time, but children categorize life into clear boxes of right or wrong, good or bad, fair or unfair. Anxious children do so because they like to know where they stand. *If I behave as I should, I am good.* There is reassurance in knowing that *as long as I follow the rules, I am in the right.* Whew! The problem is that if I have gone against them, there is only one option left. I am bad. And because lying is bad and because I lied in keeping this secret, I am bad.

My uncle had not only violated my body, he had introduced this hypothesis and its forgone conclusion into my life. I had done everything I was supposed to do and been the "good boy" that I was supposed to be, until that day and those subsequent ones where my uncle took control and altered our course through his actions.

Once again, as I allowed anger to step forward, I could see where it had been deferred and boxed through so many other similar incidents in my life. Every time I had done what I could, but the result was in doubt. Every time I had acted with the sincerest of intentions but found others questioning them. Every time I strived to be "good" but felt the judgment of others. Every time, I tried to be in control of myself but encountered others taking that control from me.

As I welcomed anger into my present, I felt other layers of it being released from my past.

Sweep it under the rug. The emotion that I had resisted the hardest is the one that had pushed the most.

Fear.

CHAPTER 17

Intuition versus Fear

Fear is another word for anxiety, and I have learned through the practice of psychiatry that when we feel anxious, we react in one of three ways:

- we try to flee or get out of a situation that makes us uncomfortable;
- we attempt to avoid or not go toward scenarios or lines of thought that bring up our fears;
- we seek distraction or reassurance by looking for ways to make ourselves feel better, either from outside sources, such as the comforting words of a friend or the fix from an addiction, or by internally rationalizing something in our favor.

An acknowledgment of my abuse to others certainly induced fear; therefore, my reaction over the years had been to avoid it. And I had rationalized this so many times through so many discussions with myself, I didn't have to address the fear head-on. There's no denying the element of not wanting to "go there," but there are many reasons for my pattern of avoidance, and these were all in response to the anxiety that I experienced at the thought of my secret being exposed.

If I were asked to describe my childhood in one word, it would be loving. Hugs were ample, kisses were abundant, and "I love you" expressions were readily available. The moments that brought up the most angst and confusion were known only to me and my perpetrator. Sure, there were other stressors such as frequent bullying in school, but my greatest moments of doubt and discomfort had everything to do with this secret. I can recall almost saying something to my parents many times, but I spent much more of my energy into covering (*sweeping?*) things up—because the best moments of my life were the ones that had nothing to do with my abuse.

Whenever I envisioned coming out with the truth in terms of relief, the tightness in my stomach seemed to be telling me to refrain. That literal gut feeling made the choice between "avoiding" and "revealing" rather clear. Why would I make the decision to taint my joyful moments with such complication? Especially when my body was steering me away.

What I now know is that there is a profound difference between fear and intuition. Fear is an overwhelming reaction to doubt and uncertainty, and our bodies, being the immensely complex machines that they are, will respond to our fears in all the ways that they can. Stomach discomfort, headaches, vague muscle aches, heart racing, shaking, sweating, lump in the throat, rapid breathing. While it may feel, in the moment, that our bodies are betraying us, these sensations are attempts to make us stop, reflect, become aware, take notice, acknowledge, understand, or release. Rather than communicating through words, our bodies must communicate through sensations.

Initially, there may be a gnawing feeling, but eventually, the body may scream in desperation through a full-blown panic attack. We owe it to ourselves to listen to our bodies. Rather than cursing your body for acting out, honor it for speaking up. And maybe even thank it for saying something.

So, when contemplating a big decision, anxiety will predictably steer us to run the other way. Our bodies then begin the cascade of sensations to help us identify fear, but we misinterpret that as further indication to flee. Furthermore, when the immediate relief from fleeing and avoiding calms the body's reaction, we confuse this with the reassurance that we made the right choice. We exhale and fool our distraught psyches into accepting that our guts had guided us well.

Intuition, however, comes in the absence of fear. After the physical sensations are endured and the commitment has been made to consider and understand the warnings that came through our bodies, if we are able to make the conscious choice to lay fear aside for a moment, intuition then has the chance to step forward.

I believe that intuition is as close as God can come to whispering into your ear. I believe that if prayer is our speaking to God, often to ask for something, then intuition is God answering back.

And where fear breaks through our awareness in the form of loud and uncomfortable screaming, intuition is an ever-present, calm, inner connection that doesn't need to yell or proclaim. It nudges with gentle clarity. It does not terrorize. If you receive an answer through fear, you may want to reconsider, defer, or even do the opposite, but if you reflect through intuition, even when the answer was not what fear had hoped for, I have found that you won't be steered wrong. Furthermore, the universe will lend its support.

All of those times when I considered saying something about my abuse to a trusted loved one—those were moments of intuition. All of those rationalizations to keep the secret—those were moments of fear.

My fears were multilayered. One of my greatest fears was to cause others pain, and I knew that if my secret were revealed, it would most definitely cause loved ones to hurt. Most of all, I was scared of my parents' reaction. Thankfully, I never worried about them doubting me. I have sat with children in my office who didn't have that reassurance. Beyond the courage that it takes to speak up, many feared their words would not matter, and that they would not be believed. I never doubted that I would be validated for my truth by my parents. Instead, with that acknowledgement of the truth, they would feel the shocking flood of emotions as their reaction. They would feel profound sadness, anger, guilt, and fear. They would feel the conflict of what to do next. There would be the reverberations on their relationship together, with family, with the community ... with him.

The ripple effects would forever alter each of us and all

of us. What would happen when other family members knew? Would they believe? Would they act? What would be the reaction of his immediate family? Could he have done this to his own children? Could my silence have perpetuated his deviant choices?

Once revealed, there would be no covering it back up. There would be questions that I wouldn't want to answer. There would be feedback that I wouldn't want to hear. There would be difficult emotions that would be shared. There would be my desire to comfort. There would be an obligation in my head to do so. There would be the resistance of having to do so and having to deal with everything all over again. There would be the reactions from my closest friends. There would be conversations within my cultural community, some in front of me and some behind my back. There would be speculation on what my life was really like, including doubts that the majority of it was truly great. There would be ramifications for me professionally among my colleagues and my patients—the potential for lost respect. There would be effects on my children, including the possibility of burdening my sweet, empathetic, loving children with angst over me that they don't need to be burdened with.

All this could happen. All this *would* happen. But beyond the rush of fear, my quiet intuition still makes the decision clear. All those years, I had protected. Protected my parents. Protected my family. Protected those around me. But in doing so, I had also protected him. And most of all, I had protected my fears. Rather than allowing for expression and release, I had tethered my doubts, my anxieties, and my fears throughout my life. Every time I felt I had let others down or caused them pain. Every time I felt my body begin to "betray" me or signal me to run. Every time I tried to control things but felt my control slip away. Every time I tried to avoid, thinking that I didn't have it in me to face it all. Every time I achieved something but didn't feel as though I deserved it.

As I allowed fear to show itself in my present, I felt it losing some of its grip on me from my past.

Helplessness.

Anger.

Fear.

On that day in the woods, I had allowed emotions to come forward. I didn't fight them. I didn't deny them. I didn't rationalize them. Instead, I welcomed them. I named them. I embraced them. And then I sent them off with prayerful intention. I had practiced the strategy that I had advised so many of my patients to try and one that I had been using over the years to release past tethers in order to live a more mindful life.

There are some experiences in our lives that are anchored by a thin wire. These are the ones that mildly vibrate when an emotion in the present resonates with a similar feeling from the past. A purposeful acknowledgement through this type of exercise cuts the wire, releases the tie. Other experiences are more traumatic. They reinforce the false stories of our lives in more profound ways. These are the ones that collect and emotionally tether us more strongly. They form anchors that are layered in their grip, as if attached by a thick cable. These are the instances where a dilemma in the present intensely pulls emotions forward with the strength of so many heavy weights from the past. These moments are certainly exhausting, frustrating, and embarrassing. But these are also opportunities. Each time the exercise of acknowledgement is performed, a layer of the cable is stripped, until eventually the last strand is finally cut, and the suffering is freed.

You can't heal completely until you feel completely. The process is painful and cannot be avoided. But the remembrance of a Divine source of inner strength ensures that you will persevere. You may hurt, but you will heal. You may fall and cry, but you will get back up again. The feelings that you thought you couldn't handle will have been overcome. Emotions demand release. On the other side of that coin, transformation awaits.

CHAPTER 18
Living a Present Life

The process of fraying cables to past emotional anchors is a tiring one. Each exercise can be draining. In fact, that is the whole purpose: to drain the emotional pool that collected from our past experiences. And the goal of untethering those feelings by allowing them to step forward may take the better part of a lifetime. Remember, the greater the trauma or the more it fed our false stories, the more layers that have to be stripped away. Because the process requires dedication, it is important that we give ourselves credit for every piece that is cut and that we remind ourselves about the worthwhile goal at the end of all the hard work. That means, rather than berating ourselves—"I have to deal with this again; this will never end"—we have to pat ourselves on the backs for each and every inch that we gain on our journeys. And the destination is the freedom to live a present life.

Life is guaranteed to have challenges, but we have it in us to deal with anything, especially if the current hurdle isn't weighed down further by the heavy burden of the past. And if we can stop ruminating about what has already happened and quit anticipating what might still come, then most of the time, the present moment as it is right now is rather calm. Maybe your present moment is even joyful, if only you could be freed from the past and be mindful of this joyful moment.

That's where we are headed.

All emotions demand release. All the energies that surround us need to be free flowing. Otherwise, negative energy that is held on to has nowhere to go, and we are still subjected to it. Even positive energy that we try to hold on to may block us from receiving further positive flow. Going back to emotions as an example, unreleased anger leads to resentment. Sadness that is held on to leads to depression. Unreleased guilt leads to shame. But even unreleased joy comes with a price. At the end of a weeklong vacation, most people waste a Sunday before returning to work lamenting that their time off is almost over—"I don't want Monday to come!" They don't want to let the joy of vacation go, but joy that is tethered leads to desperation. Instead, we would each be better off fully experiencing whatever emotion has currently presented itself, acknowledging it, passing it on, and then awaiting the next, which may perhaps be joy once more. Yes, it's hard to do, but oh how great it would be!

Over the years of practicing psychiatry, I have witnessed people successfully strip away layer by layer their emotional cords that bind. The usual course begins with a powerful Moment of Insight that the past is holding them back. This is followed by a strong push to challenge their past stories while feeling the momentum to begin new ones. The next few sessions are spent recounting how triggers were identified with greater clarity—by simply calling them out as examples of past patterns of thinking, they felt more empowered. However, at some point, most people find their trajectories of self-improvement slowing down, and in almost every case, the greatest hindrance comes from incidents of the past that involved other people. People struggle the most with letting go when their emotions are tied to the actions or reactions of others. This dilemma ultimately leads many patients wondering, "How can I forgive?"

As has often been said, forgiveness doesn't mean forgetting what was done to you. It also doesn't mean that what happened was right or okay. It means that the action or situation no longer impacts you emotionally like it used to. It also signals that your present day is not subjected to a past wrong. It no longer holds you back or keeps you from moving forward fully. It sounds wonderful, and it is essential for the goal of living in the now ... but is it truly possible? I have watched others forgive, and I have forgiven people in my own life, but I have also come to accept that forgiveness for some transgressions may take a lifetime as well. Even after layers of a cable have been stripped, forgiveness seems to be that last, thin string that can be the hardest to cut.

The process of forgiveness (and I do see it as a process) is again a tiring one. It may take more dedication than any other exercise in our lives. And there are so many levels of complexity to it. Does forgiving mean absolving the other person from having to deal with what they did or from feeling the turmoil of its consequences? Does the violator even have to take responsibility for what he did before you can forgive? Is it possible to forgive if the perpetrator doesn't express remorse? Does all of it require a face-to-face discussion? What if that's not even possible? When taken as a whole, the concept of forgiveness is overwhelming and daunting, which is why there is a need to break it down into stages.

Before we can release any emotions over the past, we have to be clear what we are upset about. What exactly are you forgiving? The answer appears straightforward in some examples but is actually very complex in others. The same can be said when determining who we are forgiving. While we are analyzing what was done to us, we need to be clear on who wronged us. Forgiveness requires an act to forgive and a person to blame.

In my own case, I must decide if I want to forgive my uncle (my perpetrator) for violating me physically and emotionally (the acts that were done to me). This is my clear identification of what I am trying to forgive as well as who I am trying to forgive.

In the case of my young patient Travis, however, the identified perpetrator and even the act of violation were less straightforward. Travis first came to see me as a child, tormented by a particular form of anxiety known as obsessive compulsive disorder. OCD is a condition in which the patient experiences intrusive thoughts, images, feelings, or sensations. These obsessions are unwanted and, often times, irrational. The person experiencing them usually knows so, but the persistence of these "stuck" thoughts causes anxiety to build and build; therefore, people with OCD then engage in certain behaviors or mental acts (compulsions) which might provide relief. Unfortunately, relief is only temporary until the obsessive thinking again returns. Travis showed me just how tormenting that cycle of OCD can be by having the courage to be vulnerable during our sessions so that I could see the impact.

There is knowledge that is taught through teachers and books, and then there is knowledge that is gained through direct experience. For me, beyond the rigors of medical school and the grueling learning curve of residency, the most impactful lessons are the ones that my patients have taught me over the years of practice. Whereas a textbook can catalogue the criteria needed to make a diagnosis, the true impact of the condition is best understood when listening to someone describe their suffering firsthand. Travis taught me so much about the day-to-day misery that comes with OCD. Not only did he teach me through his descriptions, but he allowed me to witness the burden in my office.

The most poignant episode of this was during a particular session in which Travis was overwhelmed by the intense images and thoughts in his head. He had been compelled to engage in compulsive behaviors since early childhood, and as is the nature of this disease, the rituals to release his anxiety had changed over that time. In his earliest years, Travis would repeatedly check in on loved ones, having to keep them in his sight or calling out to them if needing to leave the room. At other times, he felt the incessant urge to repeat words or noises that were said around him. There were times when he had to count, tapping a particular number of times or arranging items in symmetry. And in this most recent phase, Travis struggled with needing to repeatedly check the things around him in order to feel safe. This started with items that could conceivably cause harm. For example, he would ensure over and over again that the stove was off, that the door was locked, or that knives were put away in drawers. But the checking compulsion had escalated to the point where Travis was convinced that if anything wasn't perfect or done just right, something horrible would happen to him or his family. Beyond brief moments of clear, rational thinking, Travis was consumed with the fear of his next mistake costing him the people he loved and needed the most. This punishment was an inevitable outcome in his mind. The dread was only a matter of when it would happen and what he would have done to bring it on.

Even as he told his story, I could see the toll of his angst building further. He exhibited every physical manifestation of panic, and the tone of his voice wavered between pure exhaustion and a heightened sense of restlessness. As I listened to Travis escalating, I exchanged several glances with his father Mark, who had faithfully accompanied him to all appointments. Over the years of practice, I have communicated with countless parents through unspoken gestures, and we have navigated a seemingly effortless understanding on when they should speak up and when they ought to let me take the lead. But the rapport with these parents also means that I have felt their despairing sense of hopelessness and their struggling pleas to find relief for their children. As a fellow parent, more than as a doctor, I hurt alongside Mark as we watched Travis's anxiety reach a crescendo of paranoia. We played off of one another's attempts to reassure Travis through our words, through the tone of our voices, and through our body languages. And while there seemed to be indication of mild relief once we came up with the next step of our treatment plan, I had never witnessed Travis's debilitating OCD symptoms to the extent that I had on that day.

At the end of the session, as Mark stood by the door and I by my desk, indicating that a plan was in place and that we were ready to now move forward, Travis found it impossible to budge. He was so frightened that his neglect for something in my office would result in catastrophe. He checked under the cushions and looked on the floor. And then he did so again. And then he repeated his steps once more. And then again. He could tell me that his fears made no sense, but then he pleaded with me to reassure him that everything was okay. He turned to Mark and asked him to double check as well. And then he did it again. He took a step toward the door, but then went back again. He made it out the door. And then he entered again. The intrusive thoughts and the compulsions to check were so forceful that I knew Travis would continue to fight them long after he left my office that day. But perhaps Travis couldn't have known how much his suffering had impacted me and had stayed with me from that day on. I never forgot it.

The pain of that day was even more heartbreaking a few years later, when I was given the news that Travis had taken his own life.

Travis had not only endured that difficult day in my office, but he had gone on to receive more intensive treatment for several years. He had achieved academic success and discovered a passion to educate others about the horrifying effects of his disease. He found a voice in turning his struggles into a cause to help others, and he had a mission which gave him purpose. However, the daily fight with OCD continued to eat away at his essence. As Travis would explain to his father over time, the rare moments when OCD was silenced were filled with optimism and relief, but these were outweighed by the darkness and bleakness that accompanied his frequent doubts. His father had witnessed the intense suffering of his child in a way that most parents, thankfully, never will. He knew how hard Travis had fought them and how he longed for relief. He had gotten his son access to the best treatments available. He had walked the tough line between reassuring his child while not enabling him. Mark had gotten professional guidance for himself and had read countless sources of information. And, as most parents who yearn for their child's wellbeing do, he had prayed.

He had prayed for God's protection over his son. So, when his son was taken from him, how could he forgive? Would he ever be able to forgive God? In his case, the one who had hurt him the most wasn't someone that S could confront directly. Nor could Mark know if He felt remorse. Nor could he ask, "Why?" At some point when you can't get an answer, you stop asking the question. Therefore, Mark put his conversations with God on hold. The church had been a sanctuary for communion, both with the gathering of worshippers who had become like family and with the Source for whom voices were raised. Numbed by the pain of his loss and disappointed by the lack of genuine comfort that the institution had given, Mark stopped going. At home, the daily discussions that Mark had had with Him through earnest prayer became more ritualistic than soulful; therefore, as his passion waned, so did his practice until he finally stopped that as well.

Mark continued the obligations of daily life. He kept himself busy with the duties of work, with the distraction of close loved ones, and with the determination to fortify Travis's legacy by educating others. He was pleasant in his interactions, and he certainly gave no outward expression of bitterness or resentment. But Mark found that the least complicated times in his life were the moments spent alone or in the company of the animals that he loved. It was one such circumstance that allowed him to have his next Moment of Insight.

Mark had always had a soulful bond with his dogs. He

appreciated their attentiveness, and he found inspiration in their being so attuned to the needs of those around them. People are often verbal to the point of being annoying, but the intense human-canine connection is greatly unspoken. Mark and his dogs communicated mostly through body language and gestures. Feeding, playing, walking, and petting were nurturing acts that deepened their bond further. Mark's companions responded to him with an abiding loyalty, and he reciprocated in kind. From a human's perspective, Mark owned his dogs, but he knew that more truthfully, he owed them. It's hard to say who was being nurtured more in those moments, but the therapeutic value of the connection was invaluable.

Mark was particularly connected to one of the dogs, a gentle and affectionate animal named Bruno. This beautiful soul had become a member of their household entirely because of Travis. At a point in his life when S was doing all he could to balance the needs of his young family, Travis had pleaded for a dog, despite the pets in the home that already required care-taking. He wanted a bond that was all his own. Travis's persistence was further strengthened by the suggestion of his therapist that such a connection may serve therapeutic value as well. And as if created for that purpose only, Bruno had done just that. In spite of the initial resentment felt by Mark for the additional responsibility, he could not deny the emotional support that Bruno effortlessly provided. While Travis would often resist and, at times, even lash out at the efforts of people trying to help him, he demonstrated a willingness to be vulnerable with his loyal companion. Furthermore, Bruno had an instinctive capacity to align with the needs of his master and judiciously provide the exact gaze, action, or touch that Travis required in that moment. Ironically, the member of the family that Mark had resisted the most became the one to whom he was most indebted. This was especially so after Travis's suicide, when Bruno would become Mark's closest living connection to his son.

As an escape after a peculiarly draining day, Mark took an extended excursion with Bruno jogging at his side. Both runner and animal had a greater than usual sense of freedom as they explored a new area of their surroundings on what was a beautiful afternoon. As most people do when trying to release stress, Mark vented the happenings of that day and their accompanying emotions in a whirlwind of thoughts. One mental image merged into another as his thoughts flowed quickly beyond just the frustrations of that morning. He felt the untamed feelings within him build with a pace that exceeded his movements until finally his body could no longer contain them, and his tears began to flow. As his thoughts and emotions reached a climax, his faithful friend suddenly stopped. Mark collapsed against Bruno's form and released what he had worked so hard to contain over these painful months. What followed next was a calm silence as Mark became aware of the beautiful scene around him. More than what he saw was what he felt. An undeniable presence within the magnificence of nature. Just as Bruno had deciphered a way through Travis's resistance all those times, Mark experienced a moment that allowed him to be vulnerable as well. He knew for certain that he wasn't alone. Not in that moment, nor had he ever been. Mark might have stopped asking the questions, but He had never left. That was the day his conversations resumed.

In our discussions since Travis's passing, Mark has also viewed forgiveness as a process. Just as his grief has taken a course through many rounds of intense emotions, his relationship with God has, too. The pace of that journey has also varied. Forgiveness may be done a little at a time in order to help a person survive, or it may be offered quickly at first pass but then be pulled back. For Mark, in the immediate timeframe of having lost his child, he experienced the emotions that allowed him to get through that initial grief: the need to educate others and the compassion to embrace those around him also hurting. But in later months, his grief and forgiveness had to be worked through differently. Moments of sadness met with times of anger; purposeful action in the company of others was followed by intense solitude. His grief and his ability to forgive may take a lifetime, and he continues to work at both, but what he and his son had taught me was our capacity to endure. His persistence addresses the next step in the process to forgive.

CHAPTER 19

The Freedom to Forgive

After identifying who we blame and what it is that we are trying to release, we are still left with several other questions to ponder about forgiveness. Why must I do so? And do I even want to? The next step means understanding our intentions to forgive.

We have absolutely no control over the actions and reactions of others (which is going to complicate the course of forgiveness no matter how we had hoped it would all play out), but you can try to remain steadfast through all the difficult times if you are clear on your motivations to forgive. Your reasons can range from the logical and practical ones (such as not wanting to act like everything is okay between you and the other person the next time you see them when you know in actuality that it isn't) to the more philosophical and intangible ones (for example, not wanting to give any more of your thoughts and emotions to something that has hurt you enough already). If you know clearly why you want to do this work, then whatever the other person does or doesn't do may hinder you less.

Again, I can consider my own situation. I know that I will never forget my abuse. The notion that I would even want to forget—to wish that it had never happened—precludes me from truly forgiving because it means that I am still tethering myself to a desperate (and impossible) hope that my past hadn't happened. There is no forgetting. It also doesn't mean that I am okay with his choice to hurt me or that his repeated violations of me were in any way right. Taking advantage of another in order to satisfy your own needs while sacrificing theirs is wrong. And there are certainly no qualifiers or rationalizations for adults hurting children. Any decision on my part to work at forgiveness is ultimately a commitment to self-nurture. To honor my own right to not be violated anymore by releasing as many emotions that were tied to those episodes as I can. To free myself of those past emotions which could otherwise impact the same types of feelings in my present life. To acknowledge my truth so that the secrecy of it doesn't weigh me down. My process of forgiveness means redirecting the energies that were trapped in replaying parts of my past and instead focusing those energies on realizing my soul's full potential.

While I have clarity now as to why I want to work at forgiveness, I can honestly say that until the last couple of years, I had no intention to forgive. I didn't really see the need for it, and even more, I didn't think I ever could. What would eventually put me on a path toward doing so was a different need entirely.

I would often see my uncle at family gatherings. As I have said, my family has always been a loving one, so hugs and kisses were readily exchanged as expressions of affection and connection. The greatest acknowledgment and security that you can give a loved one is the embrace that lets them know "I see you, I love you, and I am here for you." I am immensely grateful for having received that type of affirmation every day through my family. Furthermore, as a gesture of respect within Indian culture, we were taught to touch the feet of your elders when greeting them. While some might see that as some kind of subservient act, I always viewed it as the offering of respect followed by the immediate and instinctual bestowing of blessings when their hands would then touch the top of my head. The one exception to all of this, however, was my uncle. My body would tense as he hugged me in front of others, and the shame that I experienced when touching his feet eventually transformed into resentment toward myself for allowing any of his tainted energy to be directed my way.

Finally, as an adult many years later, I called him after another family gathering. I told him that I no longer wanted him to touch me; in fact, I no longer wanted any acknowledgment between us. It had taken so much effort, resolve, and, yes, courage to make that call that day. Then all of that was violently siphoned out of me when he replied, "I'm confused. Why?"

In the brief pause that it took me to respond, I heard years' worth of reactions attack my mind, as if he was assaulting me all over again. From the enraged adult's "How dare you!" to the meek child's paranoia of "All of that did happen, right?", what finally came out was "You know why ... for everything that you ever did to me for all those years."

I can now speculate what may have gone through his own head over the course of the next pause, but at the time, I was focusing on not letting my internal turmoil be reflected in my quivering voice, and I was bracing for the next jab that may come my way. That jab came in the form of a question, "So, you don't want me to say anything to you when everyone is around?"

I am thankful that even at the time, I saw his tactic. He wanted me to doubt and second guess my plan. He wanted me to see the awkwardness of the next gathering in my head, and more importantly, he wanted me to once more assume responsibility for what everyone would feel by again assuming responsibility for harboring our secret. This time, however, his audacity sparked my own. "Yes ... and stay away from my family as well."

And that was it. The anticipation of what could happen next didn't matter. The physical drain that collapsed my body onto the chair beneath me didn't matter. Even the idea that he wouldn't comply didn't matter. For just that moment, I felt free.

The only other time that I had ever felt that way was when I told my wife about my abuse. It was that same sensation of breathing deeper than I ever had. It was that same feeling of my soul expanding. It was the same reassurance that all would be well. In the scenario of confiding in my life partner, so much of what I felt was fortified by her gracious and loving response. But in the act of confronting my abuser, the sensations that I felt were despite his twisted and manipulative response. The involvement of the other person couldn't have been more exponentially different, but the peace that I felt was exactly identical.

I had acknowledged what was done to me despite the rush of overwhelming emotion telling me not to. I had challenged the force of Fear (which in the world of psychiatry, we would call Anxiety). Rather than listen to Fear's loud command telling me to run, I had responded instead to Instinct or God's whispering nudge, encouraging me to step forward. And in doing so, I had honored the innate worthiness of my soul. In each instant, I felt truly aligned. A brief moment when the person I thought myself to be reflected exactly who my soul knew itself to be.

I didn't know any of that at the time. I just knew that I felt better in those two instances than I ever remembered feeling before. And I knew that I wanted to feel it again as much as possible.

I am further in that goal than I have ever been. That realization in itself gives me great comfort and peace. I recognize that I'm not yet there completely. Just as I fully expect that the ramifications of others finding out my secret through this book will trigger the tethers that are still there. That scares me. But on the other side of those dilemmas still to come, there is the opportunity for my soul to expand even more. At least now I have tasted that sensation, and my craving for it soothes my fear.

Without the comfort of that notion, why would I unravel what I had worked so hard to bury for half of my life? Through all of my efforts to hide a secret and create a narrative, it turned out that my own false story had hurt me the most. Instead, the authentic story that I am a Spark of the Divine despite what was done to me or what I myself have done assures me to push through.

Why would I risk my loved ones hurting? Through all my efforts to protect the feelings of those I cherish, perhaps my own false story has actually hindered how much more authentic my relationships with them could be. Maybe my intention to protect was working against our soulful contracts to learn from one another, to support one another through all the moments of this life, and to remind one another that we are still Divine.

Why would I risk confrontation? Through all of my efforts to cover things up, my false story intertwined with whatever narrative my uncle had used to justify his choices and his insecurities. My intention to reveal is not to seek revenge or even to hurt, and I no longer wait for an acknowledgment or an apology. He pulled me into his story, but I have continued to tell the false version of it within me. The result has been covering up the divinity of who I really am, and that is a sacrifice that I am no longer willing to make.

My intention to work through this process is multilayered, and forgiveness means many things to me. It indicates that I'm further along in the process of not feeling like a victim. It means that I'm not affected in my daily life. It signals that I am further fraying the cables that have stemmed from those acts and that have emotionally held me back. It acknowledges the hard work that it has taken to do so. Most importantly, though, forgiveness means that I am freeing myself to make full use of my present moment. Because right now, my soul is already the person that I have been working so hard to become. I had just forgotten it.

CHAPTER 20
Wielding Hope

What now?

In all the years of practicing psychiatry, no one has ever entered my office with the stated intention to transform, although everyone hopes to find change. From that very first Moment of Insight came the idea that this way of thinking, feeling, or behaving isn't working; therefore, they come to change those things. To change their circumstances, to change how they feel, to change some ongoing misery in their lives. But beyond the desperate search for change in order to be unstuck from the present state, there is the potential to move through suffering in order to evolve.

What do you want to do with your suffering? Do you want your moment of intense hurt to be one of many such moments in the course of a lifetime? Or do you want your suffering to be the vehicle that moves you forward? After all, why do all the work of unpacking your emotional baggage, of releasing past anchors, or of rewriting your stories if there isn't some long-term payoff. None of this is easy. The patients I have seen evolve the most are the ones who put in the most work. And let's face it—no one works just for the sake of working. They do it because there is some greater gain on the other side, beyond just surviving this moment. When we lose sight of that, we become hopeless. As a psychiatrist, oftentimes the most important task I have is to remind my patients about their opportunity, during their darkest times, to transform, to evolve, or to renew. The most important role of a psychiatrist is to offer hope.

Hope is the potential for something good. This is the reason why the quest to not just "get better" but to *understand* life itself has to start with a premise of goodness.

Why do bad things happen? Because there is the hope of something good to come from it.

Why should I bother to work on myself? Because there is goodness within me that deserves to be recognized and honored.

That's what my grandfather gave me when he took my hand in his, placed it over my heart, and reassured me that God resides within. As a child, one of the simplest prayers taught is that "God is great, God is good ..." If that God then resides within me, each of you, and all things, then at the core of everything is greatness. If I am a Spark of the Divine, then I instantly have hope. And hope isn't a proven fact. It's a belief. It's a hypothesis for good that is worth exploring further. It is a possibility that can sustain me for another day.

What I have learned through psychiatry is that the heaviest burden of negativity can be chipped away with even the slightest sliver of hope. In my office, that hope may come through a diagnosis that explains what a patient is going through. It may come in the form of a treatment option that could provide relief. It may come through validation of being heard. It may come through connection and through the reassurance that no one is alone in anything that they have ever felt. If there were no perceived possibility of something good ahead, why would a patient even come back for a return appointment? Hope comes in many forms, and the smallest example of it is still powerful.

One place where psychiatry and spirituality intersect is in the notion that even with the heaviest of burdens, there is no place in one's life for shame. Hope is the possibility of good; whereas, shame is remorse over the belief that at one's core, there is nothing good. This is why shame has to be addressed first as the basis of any endeavor to transform.

No matter what I am feeling, no matter what mistake I have made, no matter what was done to me, no matter what thoughts I have had, I am a reflection of pure benevolence. I am navigated through all of my hardships by a Divine purpose. I have the capacity to love and be loved that goes beyond any false truth that my mind has convinced me of or that my heart has felt. With that powerful understanding of life's greatest truth, I can deal with any circumstance.

When you conquer shame, you automatically bring forth hope.

Almost every person who has entered my office has been able to acknowledge their feelings of shame, but not everyone can identify the essential role of hope. I've had patients tell me that desperation finally led to their making an appointment to see a psychiatrist, yet I would answer that it wasn't the desperation that accompanies suffering which led to that moment; it was the possibility of relief that brought them in, even if it was a faint possibility.

Just as it is so important to call out anxiety or fear, we must call out the hope in our lives. When fear presents itself in any given situation, we reflexively respond to it. We feed it in all the ways we have trained ourselves to do. We do this out of habit and without even realizing it most of the time. But when you call it out, you give yourself the awareness of it, which then gives you the chance and the choice to not feed it further. Similarly, without recognizing the presence of hope, we tend to ignore it out of habit, or minimize its power. But when you call upon it, you wield it purposefully. Otherwise, it's like carrying around a weapon that you never think to use, even when being attacked.

Remember, treatment, or transformation, comes through a two-pronged approach. It involves capitalizing on a Moment of Insight that questions your false story so that you can start deconstructing it: "*I am not worthy ... I deserve to feel shame.*" At the same time, it means introducing a second hypothesis: "*I have the hope that there is something good about me,*" and then broadening your filter to collect data that supports this theory as well. Because the first theory has had a lifetime of skewed data from our childhoods to prove it into "truth," we have to fortify ourselves through hope as we start challenging it. In other words, we have to start with the belief that something good within you is even possible.

Hope.

————••————

Every patient who has survived found hope. The ones who evolved the most became proficient in using it.

Jay, the young boy who suffered from panic attacks, had no hope when his mother first brought him against his wishes. But in being able to identify fear's false alarm and in using strategies to counter his overwhelming thoughts and restless body, he gained the hope that *"this, too, will pass."*

Emme had been so burdened with shame that she inflicted herself with pain. However, her willingness to explore her five gifts led to the hope that she possessed innate value and worth.

Nadia had become so hopeless that her only desperate option seemed to be suicide. But the maternal instinct to spare her daughter's false assumption for her well-being sparked the hope that her own life story may have been based on a lie.

Travis carried the weight of his OCD for as long as he could through the hope that he would find relief and that his own suffering could help others. Mark has the determined hope that his son's life will save and inspire others, while he counts on the hope that Travis has found the peace that he had prayed for.

Hope.

If the opposing force to love is fear, then the greatest manifestation of love and the strongest weapon against fear is hope. Fear causes us to *what-if* the present circumstance and to dreadfully anticipate what lies ahead. Hope reassures that all that is needed to deal with a current situation is within each of us, and it redirects dreadful anticipation into excited possibility. Fear dictates that the latest challenge will shamefully be the worst; Hope encourages that even the worst dilemma could be the greatest opportunity for growth.

Hope.

Hope helps us reframe why bad things happen to good people. Fear would convince us that we are being punished for not being good enough. It would build on the doubt that comes with shame, which would have us believe that we deserve misery. Cynicism goes a step further; it would make the case that there is no order to bad things happening at all, as if there is only random luck to explain what goes on. But hope asserts that nothing is random and that even the worst suffering has some Divine purpose. In that Cosmic Coffeehouse, my higher self didn't sign a contract with the absolute conclusion that I would be abused, but it entered into an agreement, which, if honored through purposeful work, could result in the evolution of my spirit.

I am making my best efforts to honor that contract, but it hasn't been easy, and I'm not done yet. While there is more hardship to come, I am empowered through hope to remember the underlying presence of love in that space. A love which I can't even comprehend through my limited human capacity, and a love that will sustain me through any predicament I am meant to endure.

I am also inspired through hope to remember that I am not alone in that coffeehouse. Each one of our higher selves enthusiastically sign these overlapping and intricate contracts, which could result in a collective evolution. I have already witnessed the evidence for that through the soulful experiences between psychiatrist and patient. An inexplicable bond forged through vulnerable, raw connection that has proven itself to be mutually enriching.

And the intention for this book is the same. I HOPE to reach every soul that needs it. The souls that were seated closest to mine in that coffeehouse and with whom I have contracted most directly, and the ones in the farthest corner of that space with whom the nudge to evolve was meant to be mutually felt through a ripple-like effect.

Hope.

No one enters my office with the stated purpose of satisfying a contract. They may come initially to get past a hurdle, to be delivered from depression, or to be freed from anxiety, but ultimately, they all want more. We all do. Ask the parent or a loved one of someone who is hurting what they hope for, and they will all tell you, "I just want them to be happy."

Countless patients have desperately hoped, "I want to be my old self again. I just want to be happy." Time after time, we are linked in our desire to be happy. But the definition of happiness is elusive. When you say that you just want your child to be happy, what do you mean? In most cases, the basis of it lies in factors that are external, and most of those are fluid. What makes me happy now may be gone in the next second. It is transient.

—••—

One more place where psychiatry and spirituality intersect is the understanding that I am more than what is happening around me at this time. I am more than what I think. I am more than what I feel. I respond to what is happening around me, and I experience my thoughts and feelings, but *I* am something other than those. What I am thinking and feeling is transient, but there is a part of me that is constant. All those parts are still pieces of *I*.

Freud understood the complexity of human behavior and personality as being multifaceted. He defined the id, the super-ego, and the ego. These are the instinctual part of the psyche, the moralizing part of it, and the piece that mediates between the two. Those are distinct pieces of the collective psyche. When learning this concept in school, I never imagined that a theory for understanding psyche would be a blueprint for conceptualizing the complexity of who I am, but I now know that *I* am multifaceted.

There is the part of me that feels, which I would consider my body. This would include my physical sensations and my emotional responses.

Then there is my mind, which incorporates all that I think; this would be the thought that I am focused on at present, and all the peripheral chatter that goes on in my head.

And then there is my spirit. That is the *I* which never dies, is always constant, and goes way beyond the person that I, and the people around me, know as "Suvrat."

Now if we go back to the goal that most of us have for ourselves and our loved ones of just wanting to be happy, we can appreciate that happiness is a fleeting experience of the mind and body. Happiness, like all emotions, demands release, which is why it is temporary. What we really hope for is a more lasting sense of fulfillment. If we want something that sustains itself, it would make sense to instead focus on *spirit*.

When people say, "I just want to be my old self again," or "I just want my old child back," what they really mean is that they want to get past their current way of thinking or feeling. Instead, we could be mindful of the fact that who we are soulfully never changed or left at all.

From the moment I came onto this earth, I have been constantly Divine. Whatever my struggle is at this time, I am Divine. Whatever emotions are throwing me off currently, I am still Divine. No matter what was done to me, I am Divine.

If we really knew that, then we could never lose hope. If we focused on that at least as much as we focused on mind and body, we would have a greater sense of fulfillment. If we nurtured our souls as much as we serve the needs of our bodies and minds, we would feel more balanced. If each of us identified the gifts of our individual souls and then purposefully used them, each of us would certainly benefit from it, but so would the rest of the world.

Everything else is just human experience. So, when my circumstances are enjoyable, I can enjoy. When I am challenged, I can experience sadness, frustration, humility, embarrassment, or anger. And then I can figure out how to deal with it. Furthermore, I am not alone in those challenges. Others have survived those same human experiences; therefore, I can, too. Everyone has a hardship as part of soulful contracts. I am not alone in having been abused. Nor is anyone else unique in his own struggle. Many have encountered illness. Millions have lost loved ones. Countless are struggling through devastating circumstances, and so many people have been challenged from birth in some way. Each and every person's hurt is valid and painful, but *we all have the capacity to endure and to evolve because the essence of who we are is a constant source of goodness and strength.* We're in this world for our souls to have human experiences, but having those experiences doesn't mean forgetting our souls.

That is the lesson that psychiatry continues to reinforce for me. We spend our lives covering up who we really are. We react to what goes on, we respond to what is done to us, and we reinforce our false notions so much that we lose sight of ourselves. But thankfully, our souls don't give up on us. They nudge us to remember, and oftentimes, the only way that we will listen is when we have to. Adversity will demand attention. Every person who found his way onto the couch in my office was being encouraged to remember.

Soul remembrance is the process of uncovering all of the layers that you placed on yourself over all these years in order to see your full Divine light again. Doing so takes a great deal of effort and requires vulnerable and truthful introspection. It means setting aside judgment. It involves feeling all the emotions that we fought hard to defer. It requires challenging our "truths." It means being persistent and purposeful. It involves daily practice on good days and bad. The investment is steep, just as the courage of every patient that I have had the privilege of treating has been. But even after all that, if you only removed one percent of the layers, you shine a whole lot brighter.

See your Spark. Embrace your hope. Be prepared for your Moments of Insight.

Your Insights

ABOUT THE AUTHOR
There are no ordinary moments...

Suvrat Bhargave, M.D. is a renowned and respected educator, speaker, and board-certified psychiatrist, specializing in child and adolescent psychiatry. His uncanny ability to relate to a multi-demographic audience has allowed his practice to reach an unparalleled level of success based on empathy, education, and empowerment. Affectionately known for his "relatable expertise", Dr. Bhargave is highly sought after to lecture locally and nationally on a broad range of topics pertaining to personal growth, effective parenting, relationship satisfaction, and mental health conditions. After completing his residency training and specialty fellowship from Duke University, Dr. B (as he is lovingly called by his patients) continued his practice in hospitals, community health, and private practice settings. Throughout the years, he has been most inspired by the impact his caring nature, education, and treatment have had on others to facilitate change and to experience fulfillment through gradual but dynamic moments of "insight and awareness". A passionate advocate for healing and empowerment, Dr. B is compelled to bring a world of change to each person one moment at a time.

To learn more about Dr. B and invite him to speak at your next event, visit drbhargave.com.

Please Review

If you found that this book enriched your life in any way, help us spread the word so that other people can have their moments of insight as well. Please write a positive review where you discovered A Moment of Insight.

CPSIA information can be obtained
at www.ICGtesting.com
Printed in the USA
FFHW011150310319